P9-DCH-534

YOUR CHAIN SAW

YOUR CHAIN SAW

by
Robert Scharff

5400 Alla Road Los Angeles, California 90009

Manufactured in the United States of America

Text prepared and book designed by Robert Scharff & Associates, Ltd.

Current Printing (last digit) 10 9 8 7 6 5 4 3 2 1

Distributed by S & S Publishing Co., Box 192, New Ringgold, Pa. 17960

Library of Congress Cataloging in Publication Data

Scharff, Robert
Your Chain Saw

Includes index. 80-52192

ISBN 0-937558-00-1

Contents

This handbook provides basic information relating to chain saws. It is not intended to replace instructions or precautions given by the maker or vendor of any chain saw that you may consider using. Additionally, while this handbook contains many safety tips, it is not possible to provide precautions for all possible hazards that might result. Standard and accepted safety procedures should be applied at all times.

What Chain Saw for Me? 1

While it was only a few years ago that chain saws were used almost exclusively by professional woodcutters and tree servicemen, today chain saws rank next to hedge trimmers, edgers, and circular saws in many home garages. The reasons for this increased use of chain saws by the average handyman are easy to explain. For example, energy-conscious home owners are cutting wood as a heating fuel. Sure, you can cut firewood with a hand saw, but the chain saw makes the task easier and saves a great deal of time.

There are many other uses for a chain saw around the home other than just cutting firewood. In yard maintenance, for instance, the chain saw can be used to prune trees, help in tree removal, and clean up storm damaged trees. It can be used to build log fences and gates for use around your home. But, if you are not familiar with a chain saw, it is probably difficult to give much thought to the other things that a chain saw can do. Chapter 7 in this book was especially written to give your imagination a nudge and start you thinking of the ways a chain saw could add to your pleasure. Of course, if you are an outdoorsman, the chances are very good that you already know how a chain saw will help to create more fun from woods activities such as hunting, fishing, and hiking. Chapter 8 will detail the making of such items as a duck blind, swimming raft, ice-fishing shack, and a lean-to shelter, plus how to "deer hunt" with a chain saw. But, before taking a look at how you can get the most from your chain saw, let us attempt to determine what chain saw is for you.

WHAT IS A CHAIN SAW?

A chain saw is a lightweight, portable power tool (Fig. 1-1) used for cutting wood. Essentially, it is composed of two units: (1) the power plant and (2) the cutting unit.

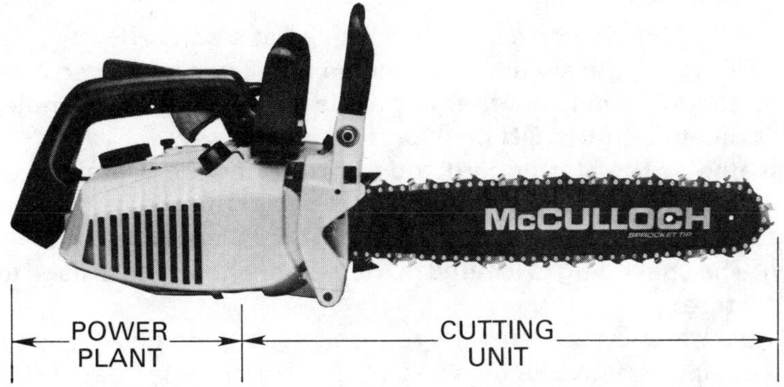

Fig. 1-1: The two working units of a chain saw.

Power Plant

Although a few chain saw models are electrically driven (Fig. 1-2), by far the most popular are those saws powered by an air-cooled, two-cycle engine. While the manner in which a two-cycle engine operates may be interesting, it is more important to understand the functions of several components of the gasoline engine (Fig. 1-3) which must work in unison if the chain saw is to run properly. These include the following:

Fig. 1-2: An electric chain saw is good for trimming backyard trees and cutting firewood near a convenient power source.

Fuel Tank. The fuel tank is normally located within the power unit of the saw with the filler cap positioned on its top. Its function is to store the fuel mixture.

Fuel Filter. Located in the fuel tank, the fuel filter is connected to the line that runs from the tank to the carburetor. It filters particles from the fuel so that they will not obstruct the fuel flow to any part of the fuel system. This filter is usually a replaceable unit.

Carburetor. The function of the carburetor is to mix fuel and air at the correct ratio. The carburetor is connected to the engine.

Idle Screw. This screw is an adjustable mechanical stop for the throttle, and it regulates the speed of the engine at idle.

Throttle Control System. The complete system includes the throttle control trigger; throttle control linkage; and, in some cases, a throttle control latch or throttle control lockout, or both. The control trigger is located in the handle so that the saw can be gripped with both hands and the control trigger can still be actuated or released. The throttle linkage itself transmits the operator's movements of the control trigger to the carburetor. The throttle latch locks the throttle partially open for easy starting.

Ignition Switch. The ignition switch is designed as a safety device to turn the chain saw OFF. That is, the switch is so located that it can be moved to the OFF position by the operator while maintaining a grip on the handle, or handles, with both hands. It must be in the ON position to start the saw.

Starter Assembly. The starter cord and return spring are contained within a housing that is usually located on the left-hand side of the chain saw. The function of the starter assembly is to rotate the engine by cranking.

Spark Plug. The spark plug is located in the cylinder head and is used to ignite the fuel air mixture.

Muffler. The muffler on a chain saw reduces the engine noise levels. When the muffler is equipped with a spark arrester, it also greatly decreases the possibilities of fire.

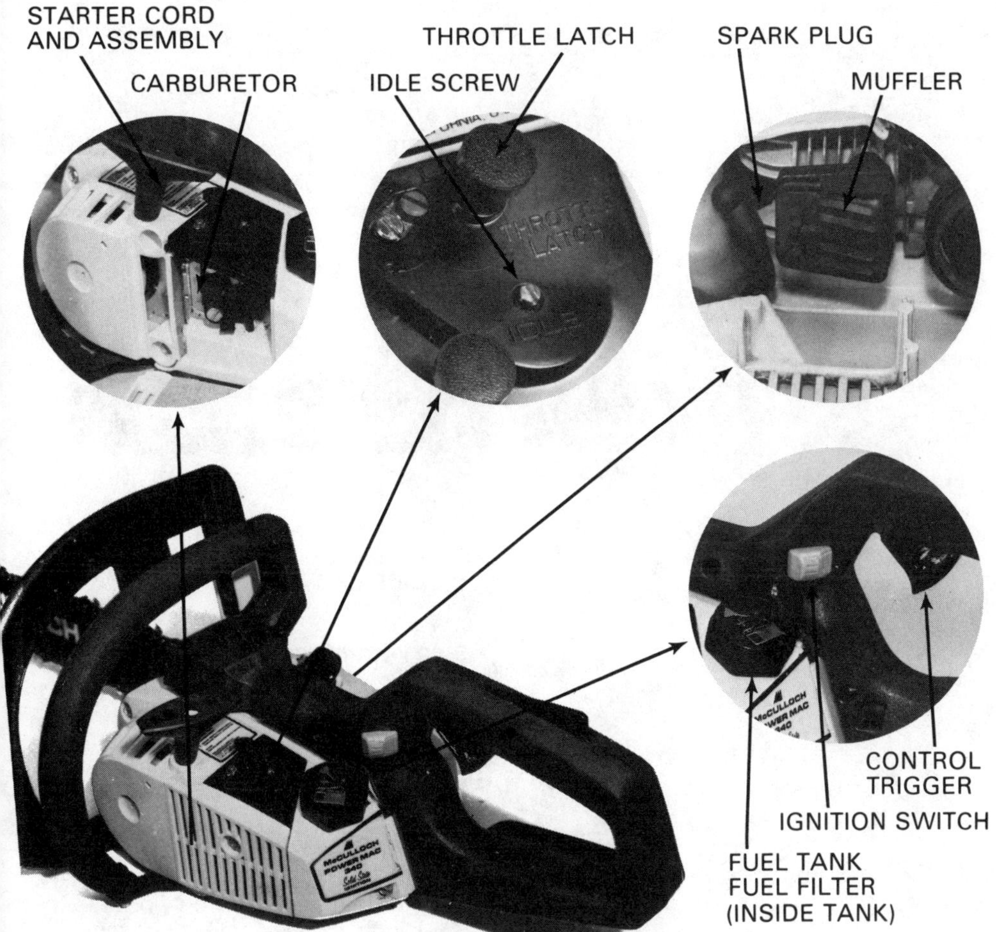

Fig. 1-3: The major components of the engine's fuel system.

Cutting Unit

The cutting unit (Fig. 1-4) consists of a clutch drum and a sprocket that drives a narrow steel cutting chain fitted with very sharp cutting teeth around a thin steel guide bar at a speed of approximately 2500 to 3000 feet per minute. Let us take a closer look at the parts of the cutting unit to see what they do.

Chain. The standard saw chain is made of metal parts riveted together to form a flexible loop. The parts that make up a typical chain are shown in Fig. 1-5. The center link, or drive link, of the chain hooks into the sprocket so that the chain can be driven around the bar. In addition, the saw chain has both left-hand and right-hand cutters. These cutters have a top plate that is sharpened to a fine edge for cutting. The side plate cutter releases the wood on the side, while the top plate chips wood out of the middle similar to a chisel. The depth gauge determines how deep the top plate penetrates into the wood each time it cuts a chip. More information on chain saw cutters can be found in Chapter 9.

Power Transmission. The power of the engine is transmitted to the chain through the use of a centrifugal clutch. As the engine is accelerated, the clutch engages the drum/sprocket assembly and the sprocket drives the cutting chain.

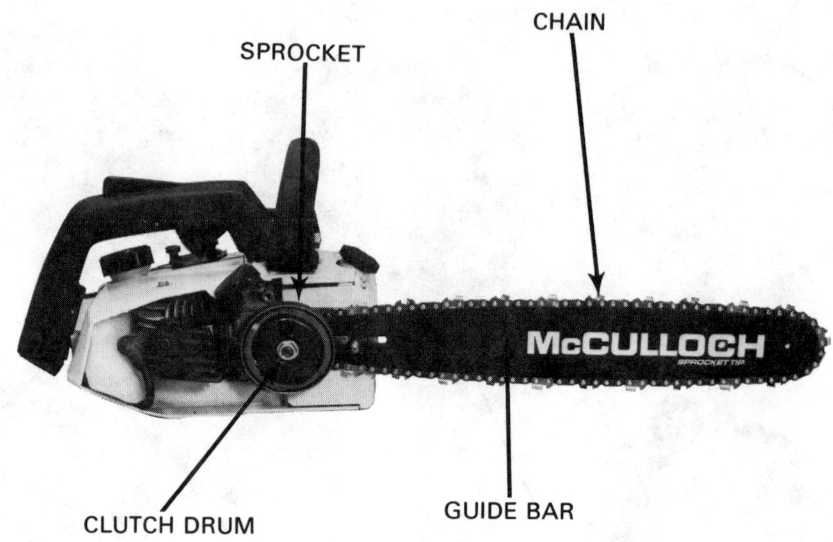

Fig. 1-4: The major parts of the cutting unit.

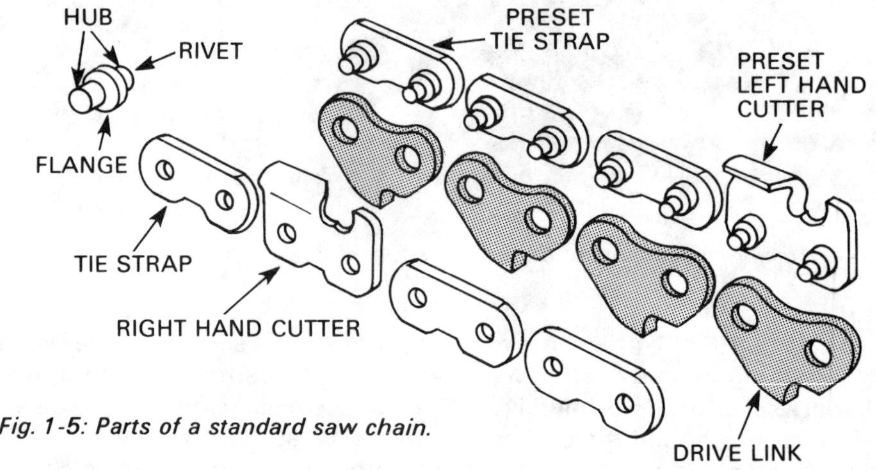

Fig. 1-5: Parts of a standard saw chain.

Guide Bar. The bar guides the chain so that a straight cut can be accomplished. Bars come in lengths of 8 to 44 inches (20.3 to 111.8 cm) and larger, depending on the intended job, and are connected to the saw by mounting lugs or bolts. As shown in Fig. 1-6, the eight major parts of the bar are:

1. **Entry.** The entry is designed to allow the chain to enter the bar from the sprocket.

2. **Oil and adjusting holes.** The oil holes allow the chain oil to flow into the groove so that the chain and guide bar can be lubricated (see Chapter 2). The adjusting holes allow the bar to be moved forward or backward so that correct chain tension can be set.

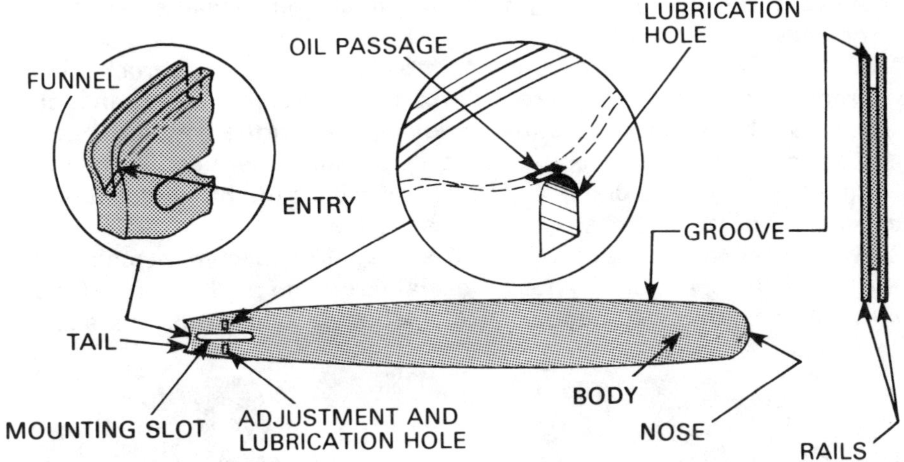

Fig. 1-6: Parts of a guide bar.

3. **Groove.** The groove is a slot in the bar where the drive links run.

4. **Rails.** The rails serve as a 90-degree guide to keep the saw chain running straight. If the rails are splayed or uneven, the chain runs tilted, causing curved cuts. Rails are normally heat-treated for longer life.

5. **Tail.** The tail is the exit part of the bar and allows the drive links to omit any dirt particles that may have accumulated in the groove.

6. **Body.** The major part of the guide bar.

7. **Mounting slot.** This slot has two functions: It allows the mounting studs to go through the bar, fastening it to the saw, and it allows the bar to move forward and backward for chain adjustment.

8. **Nose.** The front of the guide bar. There are two nose type designs available: sprocket-tip and hardfacing (Fig. 1-7). The latter, which can be used only with a solid bar, is a nose which has been heat-treated and hardened to reduce wear on the guide bar from the rotating chain. The sprocket-tip, which can be used with either solid or laminated bars, contains bearings in the tip which reduce chain drag, or friction, and enable the saw to cut faster with less wear on the bar nose. Because of these advantages, the sprocket-tip guide bar has become a favorite for homeowner use as well as farm and professional applications. Normally, the bearings of a sprocket-tip bar are lubricated with a small grease gun.

Fig. 1-7: Two major types of noses used for the guide bar: sprocket-tip (left) and hard-facing (right).

There are three other parts (Fig. 1-8) with which every owner should be familiar. They are:

1. **Clutch cover.** This cover protects the clutch drum and sprocket mechanism from any damage, helps to keep the operator from getting his hands caught or cut in the chain, and directs the wood chips out of the bottom.
2. **Tension adjustment screw.** The tension adjustment screw fits into the adjusting hole in the guide bar (Fig. 1-6) and moves the bar either forward or backward so the correct chain tension can be set.
3. **Bumper spike (or dogs).** The spike is a saw-like attachment mounted next to the bar so the operator can hook the chain saw into the log or tree for better control while cutting. With many saws, the bumper spike or dogs are optional accessories.

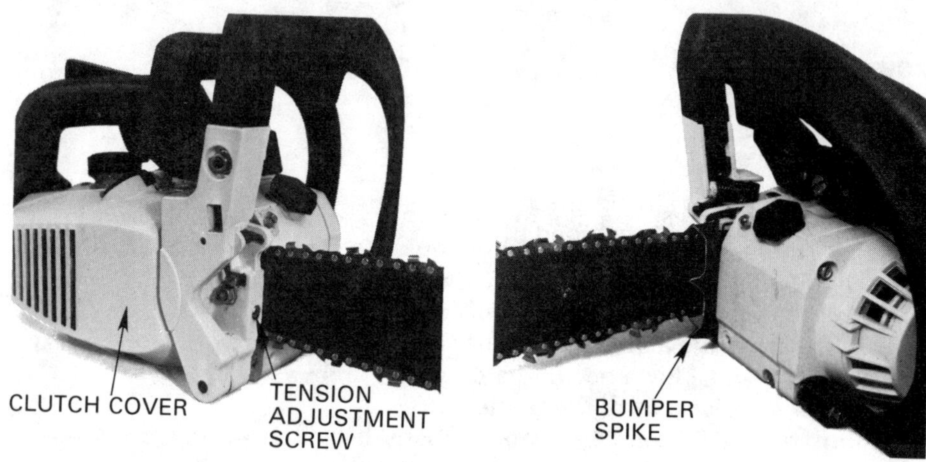

Fig. 1-8: Other parts of a cutting unit.

HOW TO SELECT A CHAIN SAW

There are literally hundreds of models of chain saws on the market. *How do you choose the right one?* It is not difficult once you decide which features you want. Then, simply eliminate those models that do not offer them.

Gasoline or Electric

As was stated earlier, gasoline chain saws are by far more popular and useful for most do-it-yourselfers. They eliminate the need for dragging around a lengthy extension cord, and they enable you to work anywhere that you can reach. Electric saws are less expensive, but your reach is limited by the length and capacity of the extension cord. Electric chain saws do not require fuel storage and are easier to start. Also, they do not produce exhaust fumes and, therefore, can be used for woodcutting and construction projects in the woodshed or basement. Electric chain saws employ the same chains and bars as gas saws. They do not, however, have the log- or tree-cutting capacity (diameters) of gas-powered saws.

Engine or Motor Size

Electric saws are generally rated in amperes. A typical small chain saw having an 8- (20.3 cm) or 10-inch (25.4 cm) bar usually has a motor that uses 8 to 10 amperes, while a medium size chain saw with a 12- to 14-inch (30.5 to 35.6 cm) bar will be equipped with a motor that requires about 10 to 12 amperes. They are designed for 120 volts AC.

Gas chain saw engines are rarely rated on the basis of horsepower as are other gasoline engines. There are so many variables that enter into such a rating as to render it practically meaningless. Instead, the various models are compared today on the basis of cubic inches of displacement of the engine cylinder (diameter of the bore times the length of the stroke). These are, of course, directly comparable and easily checked.

Guide Bar Length

While there is a tendency among professional woodcutters to use shorter and shorter bars, it is best for the average do-it-yourselfer to get a bar that will make it possible to do the majority of the cutting in two cuts (Fig. 1-9). A 12-inch (30.5 cm) guide bar, for instance, will halve a 24-inch (61 cm) log in two passes.

When selecting bar length, also keep in mind that chain saw engines can frequently be fitted with guide bars of several lengths. As a rule, the range of bar options is usually based on the engine's power, as well as balance. To avoid underpowering or overpowering the saw, it is best to select a guide bar length within the range as recommended by the manufacturer.

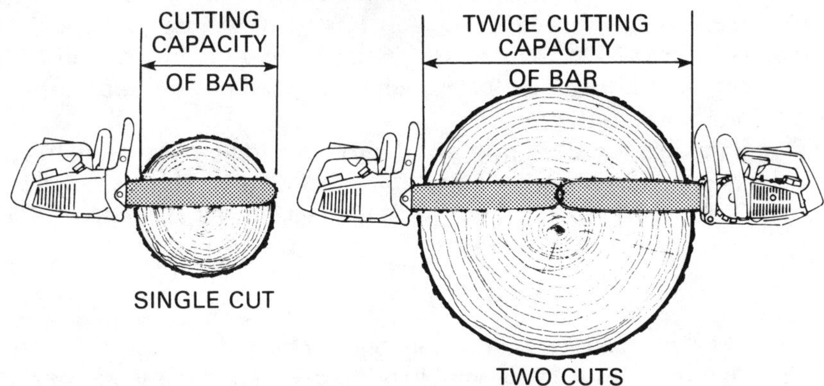

Fig. 1-9: Ideally, the guide bar should have a cutting capacity slightly larger than the diameter of the largest wood to be cut (left). Actually, a tree can be cut which has a diameter larger than the cutting capacity of the bar.

Many manufacturers classify their gasoline saws in groups or series (Fig. 1-10). Although there are no "official" standards, the basic groups are mini-saws, lightweight chain saws, medium-duty chain saws, and professional chain saws.

Mini-saws generally have an engine displacement of about 2.0 cubic inches (32.8 cc.) and are equipped with 10-, 12-, or 14-inch (25.4, 30.5, or 35.6 cm) guide bars and chains. Their weight (including the cutting attachment) is from about 8 to 12 pounds (3.6 to 5.4 kg). Mini-saws are light, easy to handle, and inexpensive. Despite the new, mass popularity of backyard chain sawing, these machines were manufactured for tree surgeons and orchardists. Even under the best of conditions, tree climbing with a chain saw is a very unsafe practice.

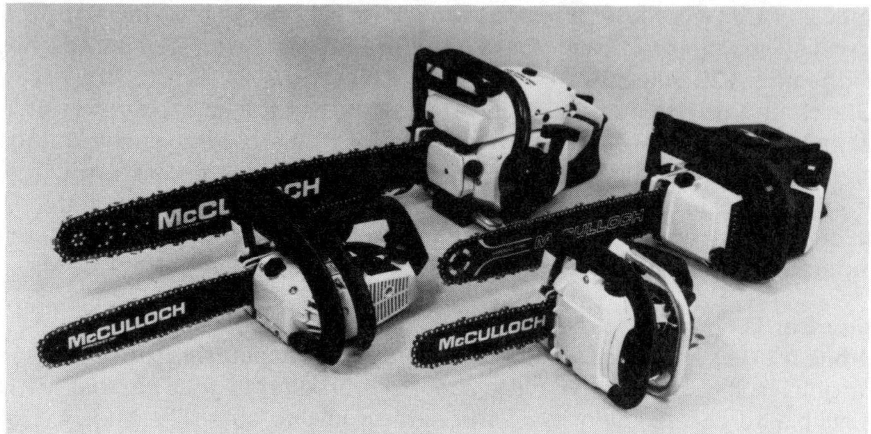

Fig. 1-10: A basic group of chain saws: mini-saw, lightweight, medium-duty, and professional.

The lightweight chain saws usually have a displacement of 2.0 to 3.0 cubic inches (32.8 to 49.2 cc.) and weigh between 10 to 14 pounds (4.5 to 6.3 kg). While they are available in guide bar lengths from 12 to 20 inches (30.5 to 50.8 cm), those in 14- to 16-inch (35.6 to 40.7 cm) lengths are the most popular.

Medium-duty chain saws generally have a displacement of 3.0 to 4.9 cubic inches (49.2 to 80.3 cc.) and weigh between 12 and 20 pounds (5.4 and 9.1 kg). Bar lengths range from 14 to 26 inches (35.6 to 66 cm), with the 16- and 20-inch (40.6 to 50.8 cm) ones being the most popular. The medium-duty saw is best for the serious amateur woodcutter.

Professional models are used primarily by the logging industry and have engines with up to 9 cubic inches (147.5 cc.) of displacement. They weigh from 15 to 40 pounds (6.8 to 18.1 kg) and have guide bars as long as 38 inches (96.5 cm) or more.

Safety Options

As chain saws have become more popular, they have also become more varied. Not too many years ago, if you went to purchase a chain saw, you had a few basic brands to choose between; having choosen the brand and the size, you had no more decisions to make. Today, however, it is a different story—there are a great many options from which you may select. While some are more frivolous than practical, the safety options should be given utmost consideration.

Kickback Protection Devices. Sometimes the chain, at the nose of the guide bar, digs into the wood in such a way that the saw violently kicks up and back. At other times, twigs may get caught in the chain or the chain may strike a foreign object during a cut. On other occasions, the top portion of the chain may become pinched. All these actions cause a momentary stoppage of the chain and result in kickback (Fig. 1-11). Kickback can be very dangerous and is one of the most common causes of serious chain saw accidents. Methods of avoiding kickback and maintaining control of the chain saw are fully discussed in Chapter 3.

Manufacturers have also helped to reduce the chances of kickback and kickback related accidents. By far, the best of the kickback protection devices is the

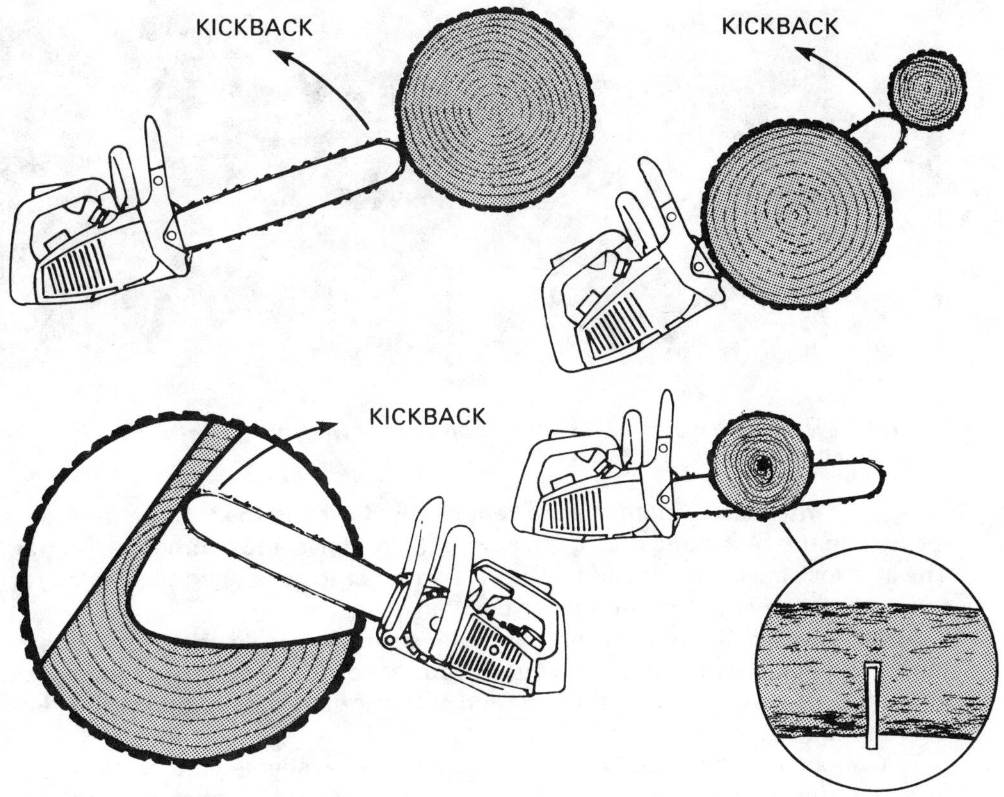

Fig. 1-11: Avoid kickback because it can be dangerous.

chain brake. While it does not really prevent kickback, the chain brake stops the chain before it can do any real damage. If a kickback occurs, the operator's hand on the front handle of the saw (Fig. 1-12A) tends to hit the brake lever, triggering the device (Fig. 1-12B) and stopping the moving chain in milliseconds. Some manufacturers offer the chain brake as an option, while others feature it with all their saws.

Another kickback protection device used by some manufacturers is the nose-guard or safety tip. This guard is a hardened steel stamping that attaches to the nose of the bar, thus attempting to prevent the moving chain from hitting any obstructions and reducing the chance of kickback. The safety tip, unfortunately, makes it impossible to cut anything with the tip of the bar, and is thus less satisfactory in the opinion of most safety experts than a regular chain brake.

Chain Catcher. Chain breakage is not a common occurrence, especially if you keep the chain well-sharpened. However, when a chain breaks, it could cause injury to the operator's unprotected hands or body.

To protect the rear hand, many saws incorporate a catcher pin near the base of the bar that is designed to intercept a broken chain whipping under the saw. As additional protection to the right hand, a few chain saws offer a right- or rear-hand chain guard.

A

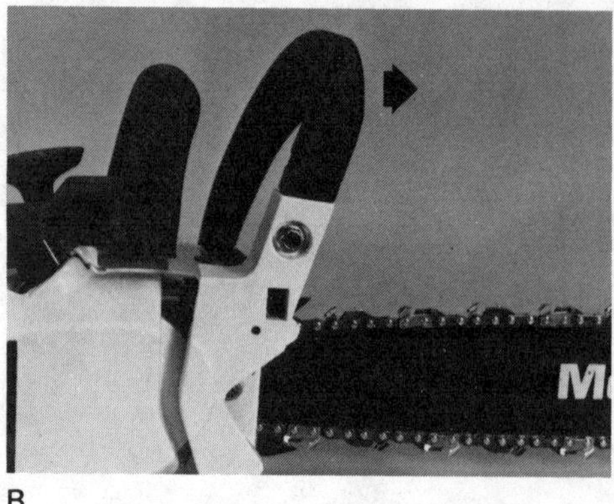

B

Fig. 1-12: (A) Position of chain brake lever when saw is working normally. (B) Position of chain brake lever when it is engaged.

Trigger Interlock. Another important safety device is the throttle interlock, located on the rear-hand grip of the saw, usually above and behind the throttle. The interlock makes it difficult for the safety trigger to be opened accidentally or when the hand is not in the proper position.

Anti-Vibration System. If you have ever operated an old chain saw for any length of time, chances are that you felt your hands tingle after the engine was shut off. This was caused by the vibration of the engine and produced considerable fatigue and annoyance.

To overcome this difficulty, many saws are now available with some type of anti-vibration system. Most of these systems incorporate rubber cushions between the handles and the vibrating parts.

Muffler Shields. With some models of saws, the engine muffler is exposed, and since it can heat up to 800 degrees F, anyone touching the muffler accidentally could receive a severe burn. A muffler shield will, of course, help to reduce the chance of such burns. The one shown in Fig. 1-13 is an integral part of the clutch cover, which, incidentally, houses all chain brake components and diminishes any possibility of accidental contact with the muffler. It also helps to prevent the possibility of igniting any dry material, such as pine needles, while the saw is operated with the clutch side next to such combustible material.

Other Optional Features

Although the safety features just described should be high on your list of priorities, other optional devices may also be important to you. Keep in mind, however, that experienced woodcutters have learned that exotic frills can be more trouble than their convenience is worth, so careful, personal consideration of the options and actual cutting conditions is a good idea. Here are some of the more popular (and useful) options available.

Oilers. As the chain moves around the guide bar in a special groove, friction builds up heat. A lubricating oil must be pumped into the groove during cutting to combat this friction. The chain lubrication is accomplished by two methods, both supplied by the same oil reservoir located under the engine.

1. **Manual chain oiler.** The manual oiler provides lubrication to the chain when a button, usually located near the throttle, is pushed.

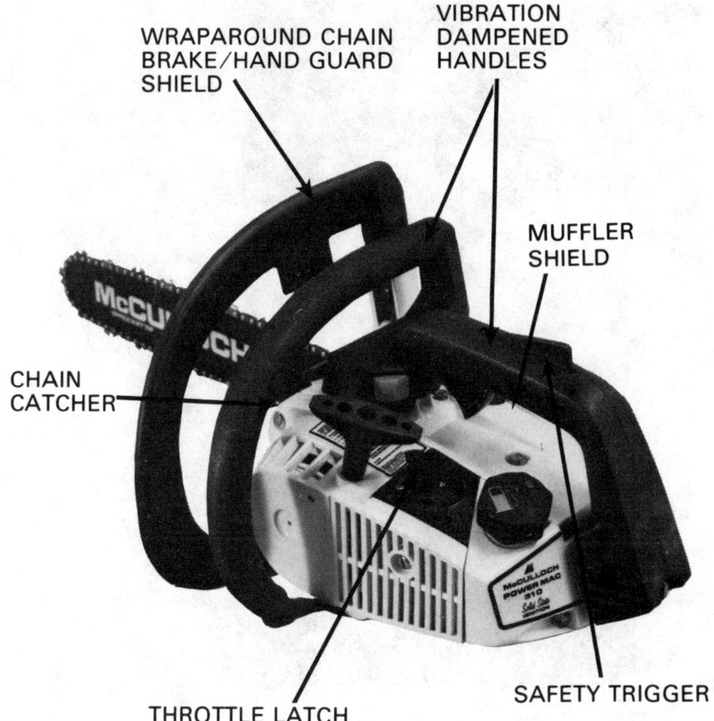

Fig. 1-13: Safety options to look for.

2. **Automatic chain oiler.** The automatic oiler provides a continuous flow of lubricating oil to the bar and chain during operation. The amount of flow is adjustable on most saws.

Some manufacturers offer both automatic and manual oiling. This is an advantage if you will be cutting in very cold or hot weather or if you will be doing a great deal of heavy cutting. Under such conditions, any additional oil can be provided by the manual oiler. The manual oiler allows you to keep cutting when the automatic oiler malfunctions.

Automatic Sharpeners. Automatic chain sharpeners are handy (Fig. 1-14). When the chain requires sharpening, simply depress the sharpener button for a few seconds with the engine running at about half speed. Depressing the button brings a grinding stone into contact with the cutting edge of the specially designed chain (see Chapter 9), restoring the edge to near peak cutting efficiency. However, even with the regular use of the automatic sharpener, periodic touch-up filing or sharpening will be required.

Electronic Ignition. Because cutting can require frequent stopping of your chain saw (while moving from one spot to another, refueling, checking chain tension, etc.), easy starting is an important consideration. The standard system used for many years with most chain saws was high tension magneto ignition. While this system was fine when it was working properly, it did require servicing and constant adjustment, as well as frequent replacement of the points and condenser. This system is still in use in some saws.

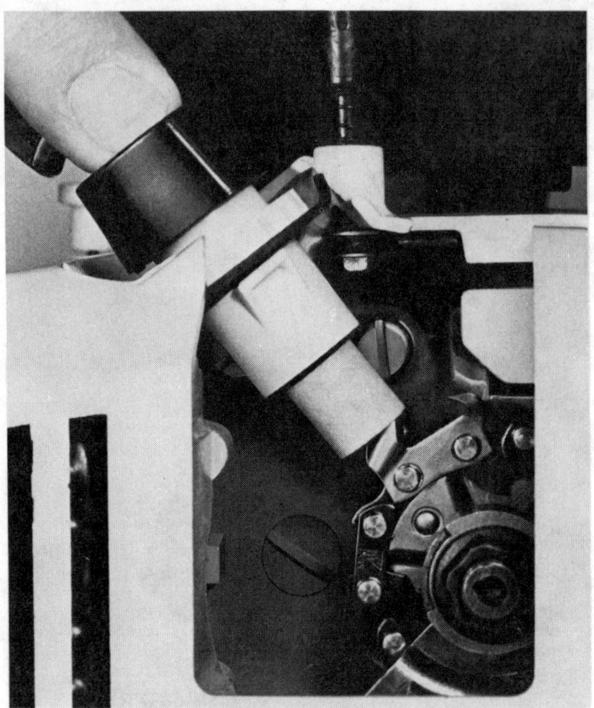

Fig. 1-14: The operation of the automatic sharpener.

Recently introduced to the chain saw field, the electronic ignition is a sealed system that does away with the condenser and the points. The timing of the spark plug remains set for the life of the saw. Electronic ignition is ideal for the occasional user who would rather not do any tuneup work and replace parts.

It is important not to confuse electronic ignition with electric start. While push-button electric starting worked well for garden tractors and lawn mowers, it never proved successful with chain saws. As a result, it is not offered as an option by any of the major manufacturers.

Compression Release Valves. The compression release valve—sometimes called a decompression valve—reduces engine compression for easier starting, and although not a necessity, it is another convenience feature, especially on larger displacement (5 cubic inches [82 cc.] or larger) chain saws. When this valve is pushed out, the operator releases some of the pressure that builds up in the combustion chamber of the engine and thus makes it easier to pull the starter rope. Once the engine is started, the valve button is released to allow the engine to operate at full compression. On some models, the valve button releases automatically when the engine fires or when pressure is applied to the throttle trigger.

Handles. In cold weather, metal handles draw heat from the operator's hands, resulting in quicker fatigue and discomfort. For this reason, most manufacturers are using either plastic or rubber-insulated handles, since they have low thermoconductivity when compared to painted steel or aluminum. In addition, plastic and rubber handles add a damping factor which reduces vibration.

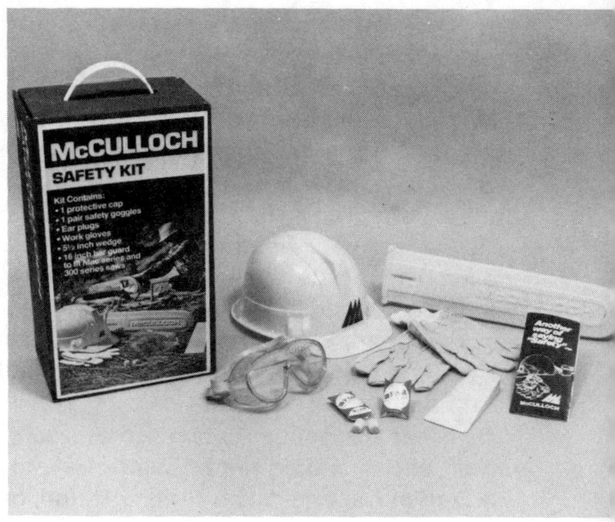

Fig. 1-15: Safety kits provide many of the items needed when using a chain saw.

Other features and conveniences are offered by the manufacturers that contribute, in varying degrees, to cutting efficiency and comfort. A "shopping tour" will familiarize you with what is available. Consider, too, another important "feature"—the manufacturer's experience and reputation as well as that of your dealer. When testing a chain saw, do not forget to examine it for quiet running, low vibration, handling ease, and balance. The latter two points are judged on "feel" and convenience of controls (on/off switch, throttle, oiler, and choke buttons). The following is a recap of the features to insist upon when purchasing a saw:

- Lightweight.
- Clean, compact styling.
- Good balance and handling characteristics.
- Convenient controls.
- Operator comfort and safety features.
- Reputable manufacturer and dealer.

If you insist on these minimum features, you cannot go wrong when purchasing a chain saw.

OTHER EQUIPMENT

Other equipment can be divided into two groups: (1) for the operator and (2) for the chain saw. Let us first look at the items needed by the operator.

Personal Attire

The clothing worn by the chain saw operator should be selected to meet two requirements: safety (Fig. 1-15) and comfort. To achieve these two requirements, keep the following considerations in mind when selecting your clothing for chain saw work:

1. Wear trim-fitting garments that are neither too loose nor too tight. Loose clothing may be caught by the moving chain or may be drawn into the engine air intake. Also, such clothing may catch on branches or other projections and

throw you off balance. Do not wear neckties, scarfs, or jewelry; wear cuffless pants, short sleeves, or buttoned shirt cuffs. Clothing that is too tight may hamper your movement and agility.

2. Clothing should be suitable for the weather. Warm, but not bulky clothes are best for winter. Lightweight clothing is preferable in hot weather.

3. Always wear snug fitting, nonslip work gloves. They will improve your grip and will also keep your hands cleaner.

4. Protect your head with a hard hat when felling trees or working in the woods. These hats, similar to those worn by construction workers, protect against falling bark, dead branches, and other debris which may be dislodged from the tree overhead. But, hard hat protection is not needed for all chain saw work. If, for instance, you are bucking up firewood in the yard, you really do not need a hard hat.

5. Wear work shoes or boots, preferably with metal toe reinforcing. Low shoes or soft shoes should not be worn. Calked or hobnailed boots are excellent for working in the woods, on rough ground, or on top of logs. Nonskid soles should be worn when the footing is slippery.

6. Protective goggles or safety lens type glasses are a must while operating a chain saw.

7. Be sure to be fitted for and wear hearing protection devices (head set or ear plug types).

Accessory Equipment and Supplies

There are a few accessory items and supplies that you should have regardless of the chain saw operation you plan to undertake. For example, except in the work area, always keep a scabbard over the saw chain and guide bar, or keep the chain saw in a carrying case (Fig. 1-16). The latter encloses the entire saw.

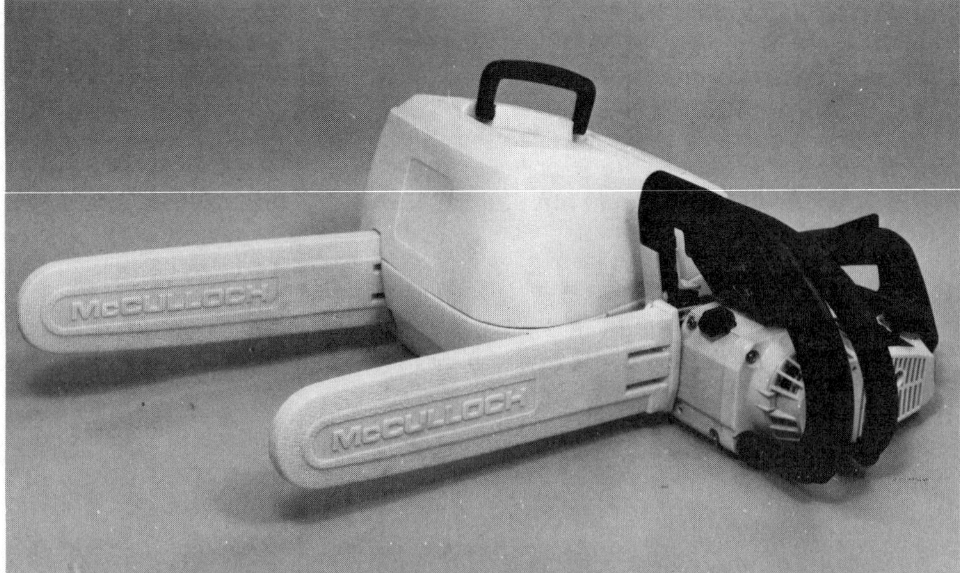

Fig. 1-16: When transporting the chain saw from place to place, be sure to carry it in a carrying case or at least cover the guide bar with a scabbard.

Fig. 1-17: A log lifter in use.

To carry a supply of fuel mixture, use a red safety fuel can(s) with a filter nozzle. Also take along oil for the chain oiler and a funnel to fit the oiler reservoir. Of course, when using an electric chain saw, you will need a properly sized extension cord and a source of electrical power. In the woods, a portable electric generator, capable of 1.2 to 2 kilowatts, is an ideal power source for most chain saws. The generator should be operated as directed in the manufacturer's instruction manual.

For many bucking and felling operations, you will need plastic wedges. **Never** use steel wedges or an axe to hold cuts open when using a chain saw.

Axes do have an important part to play in woodcutting. They are made in various patterns and head configurations (see Chapter 5). Their heads are usually forged from carbon tool steel, and the blades or bits are heat-treated. Head weights vary from 1-1/4 to 5 pounds (.6 to 2.3 kg), with hickory handles ranging from 14 to 36 inches (35.6 to 91.4 cm) long. The double-bit axe is usually used to fell, trim, or prune trees and to split and cut wood. It is also used for notching and shaping logs and timbers. The single-bit axe may be used for the same purposes; in addition, the poll is used to drive wood stakes. Hatchets are used for cutting, splitting, trimming, and hewing; nails and stakes may be driven with the striking face. A cant hook or log lifter (Fig. 1-17), a logging chain or cable, a string (to a plumb tree), and warning signal are other items you should have when working in the woods.

A few simple tools (screwdriver to fit the chain-tensioning screw, spark plug wrench, grease gun if required for roller-nose, chain sharpening kit, and wrench to loosen nuts on saw) may be needed for chain and saw maintenance. It is also good to have the following "spares" on hand: proper spark plug, air filters, starter cord, and an extra loop of sharpened saw chain. Under a dry woods condition, a fire extinguisher or shovel should be available in case of fire. A first aid kit should also be taken along. If cutting is to be done in an area where snakes are present, carry a snake bite kit. Snake boots and proper bite care are the best defenses against poisonous reptiles.

Before Operating Your Chain Saw 2

After purchasing a chain saw, there is a great temptation to immediately try it out in actual cutting. This is *not* recommended practice. It is far better to first become thoroughly familiar with the controls and with the necessary fueling, starting, and adjustment procedures. This is true even if you have owned a similar chain saw from the same manufacturer in the past. Different models may have markedly different requirements.

The information in this chapter is of a general nature, applicable to most chain saws. For specific data on your chain saw, check the owner's manual that came with it. Study the manual carefully, paying particular attention to the location and operation of the controls on your saw, the things to be checked before it is operated, and the recommended fueling and adjustment procedures. By using the owner's manual along with this book, you will be able to operate your chain saw effectively and safely.

FUEL AND LUBRICATION

For safe and smooth operation of your chain saw, proper fueling and lubrication are "musts." Because a chain saw has a two-cycle engine, the fuel required is a mixture of gasoline and motor oil. Never operate a chain saw on gasoline alone. The two-cycle engine receives its only lubrication from the fuel mixture.

In addition to the saw's engine, its chain and guide bar also need lubrication. Remember that the chain turns very rapidly on the guide bar, and both parts are made of metal. Thus, if not properly lubricated, the metal-to-metal friction at high speeds will ruin the bar or the chain, or both. Proper lubrication is usually accomplished by keeping a chain oil tank, which is located on the saw (Fig. 2-1), filled with the correct chain oil.

Fig. 2-1: Typical locations of a fuel tank and chain oil tank.

Fueling

When fueling a chain saw, having the correct ratio of gasoline to oil is very important. Since the manufacturer's specifications vary anywhere from a 20-to-1 gas/oil mix to a 40-to-1 mixture, it is necessary to follow the recommendations for the proper mix in the owner's manual. Of course, a 20-to-1 mixture means that twice as much oil is used when compared to a 40-to-1 ratio. Keep in mind that there will be less smoke created if the gas/oil ratio is higher, resulting in less carbon accumulation. Carbon build-up causes wear which will eventually result in problems. There is still another benefit of a high gas-to-oil ratio mixture. The spark plugs will not foul as readily as plugs in engines where the mixture calls for more oil. For this reason, some saw manufacturers have a special two-cycle custom oil available which permits the use of a higher gas mixture ratio—for example, a 40-to-1 mixture rather than 20-to-1. To get some general idea as to the amounts of gas and oil involved in making either a 40-to-1 or a 20-to-1 mixture, consult the following table:

FUEL MIXTURE TABLE

Gasoline	40:1 Ratio—Oil		20:1 Ratio—Oil	
½ U.S. Gal.	1.6 oz.	48 ml (cc)	3.2 oz.	95 ml (cc)
1 U.S. Gal.	3.2 oz.	95 ml (cc)	6.4 oz.	190 ml (cc)
5 U.S. Gal.	16.0 oz.	475 ml (cc)	32.0 oz.	950 ml (cc)
1 Liter	0.9 oz.	25 ml (cc)	1.7 oz.	50 ml (cc)
5 Liter	4.3 oz.	125 ml (cc)	8.5 oz.	250 ml (cc)
20 Liter	17.0 oz.	500 ml (cc)	34.0 oz.	1000 ml (cc)
1 Imp. Gal.	4.3 oz.	125 ml (cc)	8.6 oz.	250 ml (cc)
2 Imp. Gal.	8.6 oz.	250 ml (cc)	17.1 oz.	500 ml (cc)
5 Imp. Gal.	21.4 oz.	625 ml (cc)	42.8 oz.	1250 ml (cc)
Mixing Procedure	**40 parts gasoline to 1 part oil**		**20 parts gasoline to 1 part oil**	

Use only regular grade leaded gasoline of about 85 to 90 octane; do not use premium, unleaded, or low lead gasolines. It must be clean and fresh. Any gasoline that has been kept on hand for more than three months should not be used.

Only clean, two-cycle engine oil should be used with a chain saw. Avoid the use of multi-grade oil products (10W-30, for example) or any other oils formulated for four-cycle or water-cooled engines. Fuel additives or special starting fluids should not be used because seals and other rubber composition parts may be damaged.

Mix the fuel in an approved safety can equipped with a flexible spout and strainer. (Never do the mixing in the saw tank itself.) Pour about half of the gasoline and all of the oil required into the mixing container (Fig. 2-2A). Agitate the contents vigorously by shaking. Pour in the rest of the gasoline and agitate the contents of the can for one full minute to be sure of attaining a uniform mixture. Thoroughly mixed fuel makes your saw run better.

When refueling the saw, place it with the bar pointing downhill on bare ground, free from grass, twigs, and other flammable objects. Allow a hot saw to cool approximately five minutes prior to refilling. This five-minute period can be used to sharpen or touch up the cutters. (Do not wait for the engine to run out of fuel be-

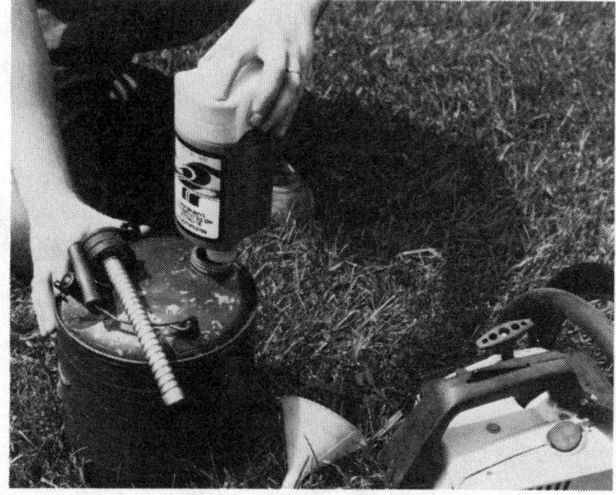

Fig. 2-2: (A) Mixing a chain saw's fuel; (B) filling the fuel tank.

fore refilling; removal of the saw from some cuts may be difficult and dangerous, and filling a tilted saw may cause spillage.) When removing the fuel cap, remember that the fuel in your saw may be under pressure; therefore, always remove it slowly. Use a clean, rust-free funnel (Fig. 2-2B) or a flexible hose to avoid spillage. Do not fill the fuel tank to the brim; and take care that no sawdust or dirt enters the tank. Clean any spilled fuel from the saw before starting the engine. Check the fuel lines and connections for leaks. Do not start the engine at the place of refueling; move at least 10 feet (304.8 cm) away. When fueling, keep a fire extinguisher nearby and, of course, do not smoke or bring any flame near the fuel.

Chain and Bar Lubrication

Always refill the chain oil tank each time the fuel tank is refilled. (Both the chain oil and fuel mix tanks are identified by raised letters.) While any brand of clean motor oil, including reprocessed oil, may be used, most saw manufacturers recommend the use of a special chain and sprocket oil. This oil is formulated with "viscosity improvers" which render it free-flowing even at low temperatures and has the property of clinging to the chain to minimize "throw-off." If special chain oil is not available, use SAE 30 nonadditive motor oil at temperatures above 40 degrees F (5 degrees C) and SAE 10 nonadditive motor oil at lower temperatures. When cutting frozen wood, dilute your bar and chain oil 25 percent with diesel fuel or kerosene. Never use dirty oil or used oil in the chain oiler system as it may damage the oil pump.

Use a clean, rust-free funnel to fill the oil tank. It is a good idea to have one funnel for the fuel and one for the chain oil; do not switch the funnels in use. Wipe down the saw if any oil is spilled on it. Keep in mind that the saw chain should appear moist with oil in the area of the connecting links.

INSTALLING THE CHAIN

With a new saw, the owner usually must install the chain—unless the dealer does it for you—before the saw can be used. Also, the chain has to be replaced from time to time. Therefore, it is important to know how to install a chain on your saw. But, whenever you are working on a saw chain, be sure to wear gloves for protection against the sharp teeth.

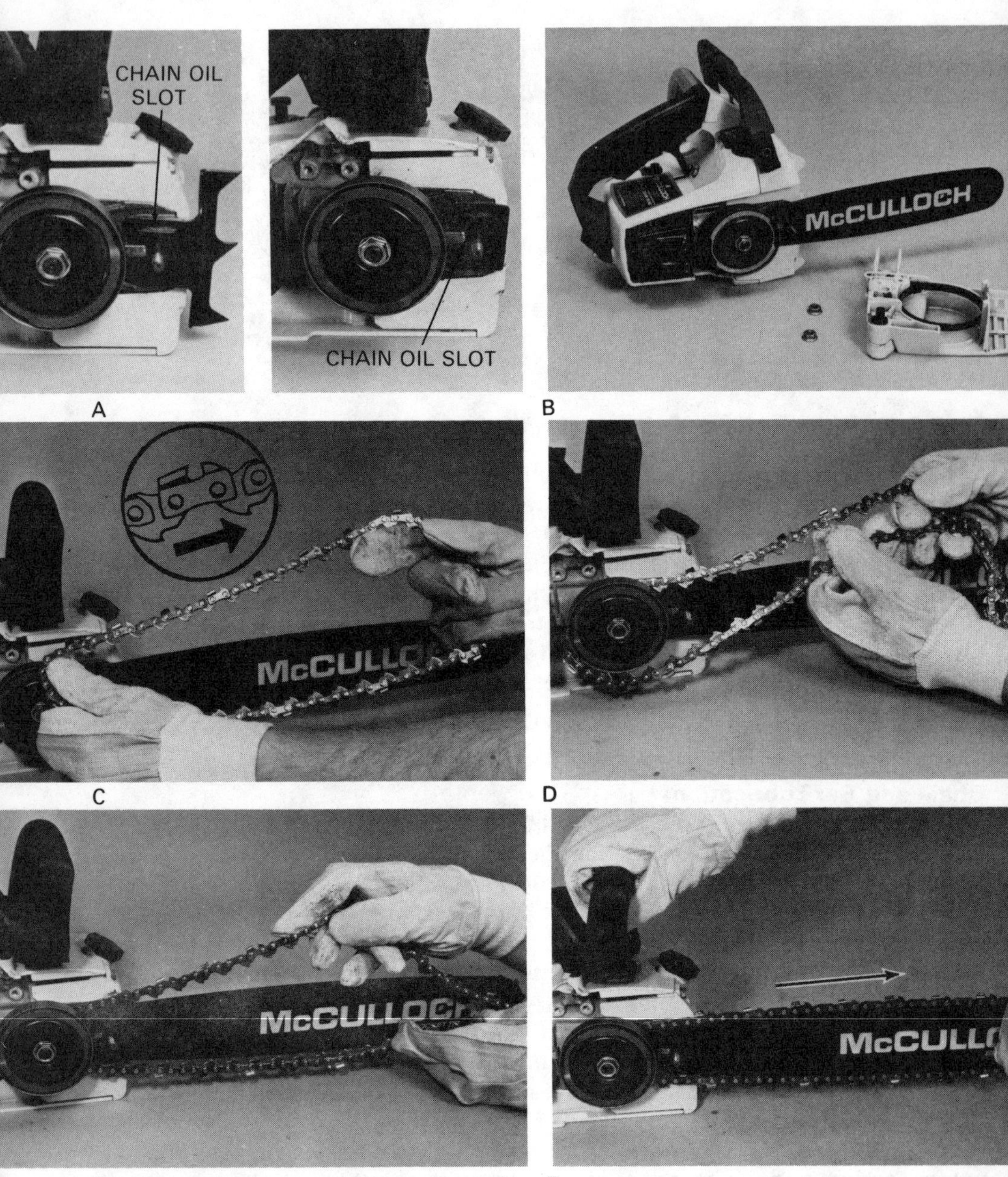

Fig. 2-3: Steps in installing a typical guide bar and chain.

If your saw is equipped with an automatic chain sharpening system and/or a chain brake, they must be removed from the saw before installing the chain. Although your owner's manual should always be followed for exact details, the following typical instructions will help to make the installation of the chain on a new saw easier. It will also help you when it is necessary to replace a chain.

1. Make certain that the ignition/stop switch is in the OFF position. Remove the bar mounting nut(s) and/or bolt(s). When replacing a chain, the bar and bar mounting pad or spike can be removed and the old chain taken off of the bar.
2. Place the bar pad spacer over the bar bolt(s) and onto the bar pad. If a spike is to be used, do not use the bar pad spacer. The pad spacer or spike will help to ensure correct alignment of the sprocket and bar. But, when installing either, be certain the chain oil slot is at the top so that the chain oil can enter the top oil passage in the guide bar (Fig. 2-3A).
3. Unpack the bar and chain. Slide the slotted end of the bar over the bar mounting bolt(s) and push it back toward the sprocket as far as it will go (Fig. 2-3B).
4. Straighten any kinks in the chain and spread it out in a loop (Fig. 2-3C). The cutting edges should face in the direction of chain rotation, which is from the bar nose toward the sprocket along the bottom edge of the bar—or in a clockwise rotation.
5. Tilt the top of the chain away from you so that you can slide it edgewise over the top of the drum (under the saw housing and bracket). Put the chain tangs into the bar groove and pull the chain so there is a loop at the rear of the bar (Fig. 2-3D).
6. Guide the chain around and behind the drum (between the drum and the muffler) and onto the sprocket (Fig. 2-3E). Move the chain back and forth to make sure it is in proper mesh with the sprocket and lined up with the bar groove.
7. To complete the installation of the chain, guide the chain center links into the bar groove all the way around the bar. Pull the nose of the bar out to take up all the slack in the chain (Fig. 2-3F). If your saw does not have a chain brake, you can adjust the tension on the blade (see next page). If the saw does have this option, it must be installed before making any adjustments.

Chain Brake Installation. When installing a chain brake, make certain that its lever is pulled back to the disengaged position (Fig. 2-4A). Then, fasten the chain brake assembly to the saw. The brake band should be fitted carefully around the outside of the clutch drum during assembly, as shown in Fig. 2-4B. **Caution:** The chain brake can be cracked or broken if carelessly installed. The chain tension adjustment nut (tang) must be properly positioned in the adjustment hole in the bar before tightening the lower retaining nut. There should be no large gaps between the chain brake and the saw housing, and the brake housing should fit snug against the bar (Fig. 2-4C).

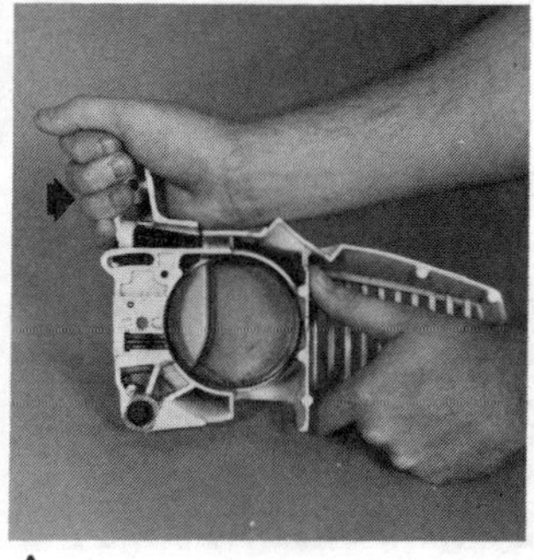
A

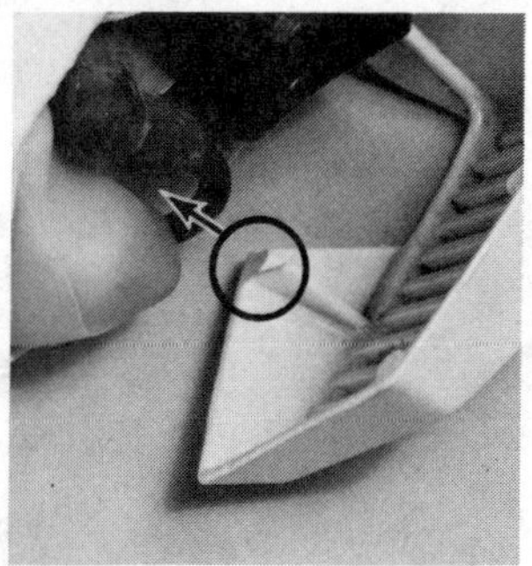
B

C

Fig. 2-4: Installing a typical chain brake.

Adjusting Chain Tension

Proper tension of the chain is extremely important. As a matter of fact, it is something that must be checked before starting any cutting operation, as well as during the job. While you should check your owner's manual for the exact chain adjustment techniques, the following procedure will give you some idea of how a typical saw chain is adjusted.

1. Turn the chain tension adjustment screw in or out to align the nut with the bar hole (Fig. 2-5A).

2. Hold the nose of the bar up (Fig. 2-5B), and turn the adjustment screw clockwise to tension the chain. It should be a snug fit all around the bar. The chain has a proper tension when, with the bar locked in the uppermost position, it has a snug fit (Fig. 2-5C) all around and will pull around the bar easily by hand. No droop or sag of the chain is advisable (Fig. 2-5D). More information on chain adjustment can be found in Chapter 3.

Automatic Sharpener Installation

If your saw is to have an automatic sharpener system, it is installed after the bar, chain, and chain brake are correctly installed. Remove the automatic sharpener assembly from its package. Then, the installation of a typical unit is basically as described here:

1. Rotate the knob clockwise until it separates from the body (Fig. 2-6A). Align the ears on the assembly with the slots in the mounting bracket on the unit (Fig. 2-6B).

2. Push the assembly firmly in place and turn the entire assembly clockwise approximately 1/4 turn or until snug (Fig. 2-6C). Using a screwdriver, place it in

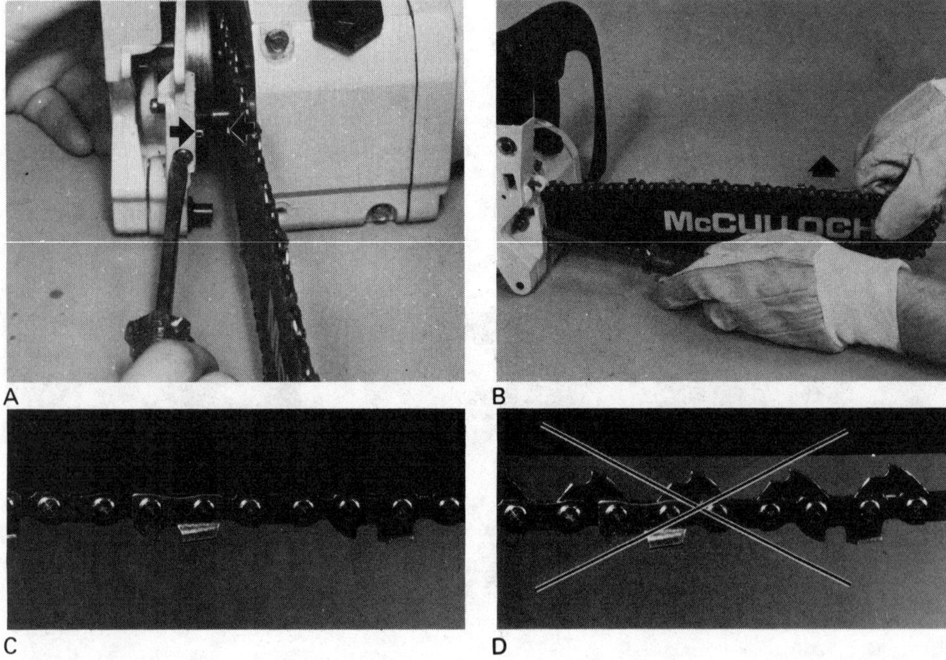

Fig. 2-5: Adjusting the chain's tension.

the notch and engage the serrations on the body. Gently continue turning the assembly clockwise approximately 1/16 to 3/32 inch (1.6 to 2.4 mm) until fully engaged (Fig. 2-6D). Do not apply too much force.

3. Place the two hooked ends of the sharpener bail in two serrations which are exactly opposite one another, also ensuring that the ends are set through the bracket (Fig. 2-6E). Holding the looped portion of the bail, swing it out and over the body (Fig. 2-6F). Then, snap the bail over the side of the body into its final position (Fig. 2-6G).

4. To attach the knob onto the body, engage the ratchet teeth, depress the knob, and turn counterclockwise a few turns until the knob and body "catch." Now, gently continue turning the knob until it will no longer turn; you are now ready to use the automatic sharpener.

OPERATION OF A GASOLINE CHAIN SAW

Before attempting to cut any wood with your newly assembled chain saw, it is very important that you know how to start and stop the tool.

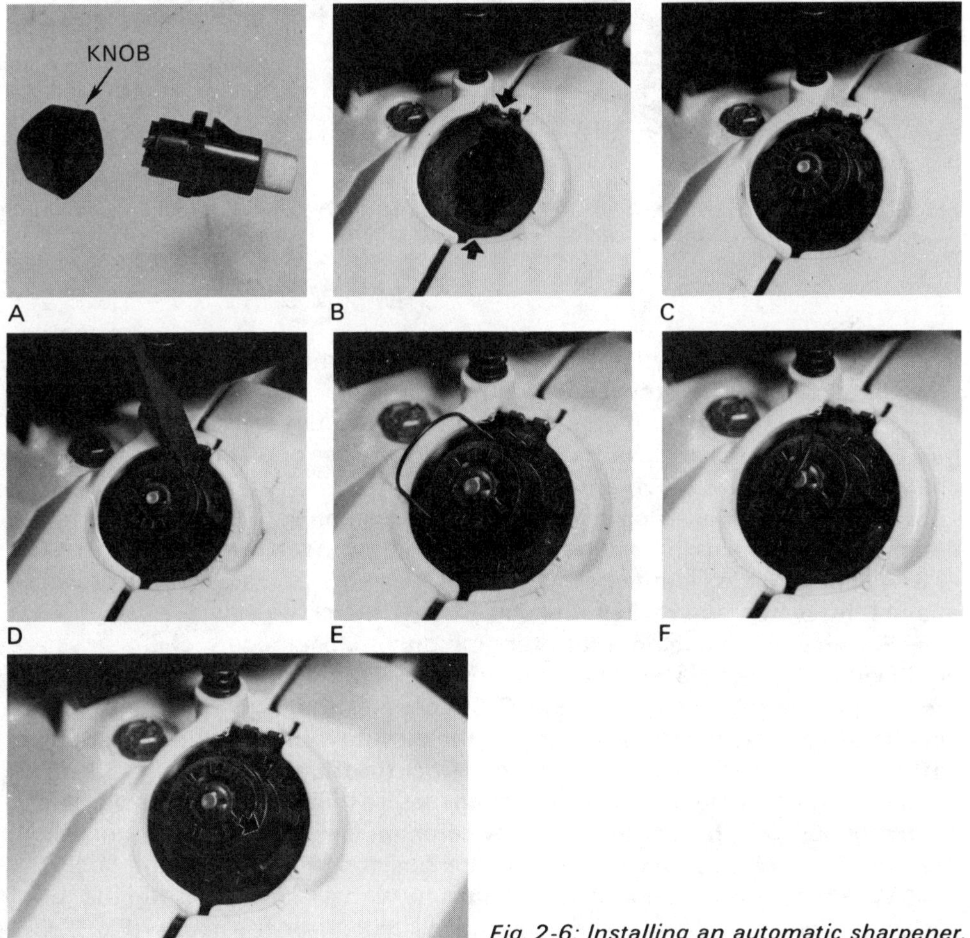

Fig. 2-6: Installing an automatic sharpener.

Pre-Start Checks

Before you attempt to start a typical gasoline chain saw, be sure to:

1. Fill the fuel tank with the correct fuel mixture. Be certain not to spill fuel on the saw (Fig. 2-7A); and, if you do, allow the saw to dry out thoroughly before attempting to start or operate it.
2. Fill the chain oil tank with the correct chain oil and pump the manual oiler until oil is seen at the top of the bar, above the bar bolt (Fig. 2-7B).
3. Make sure the chain has correct tension and the bar is tight on the saw.
4. If the saw is equipped with an automatic sharpening device, never start or operate the tool unless the device or its cover are properly positioned.

A

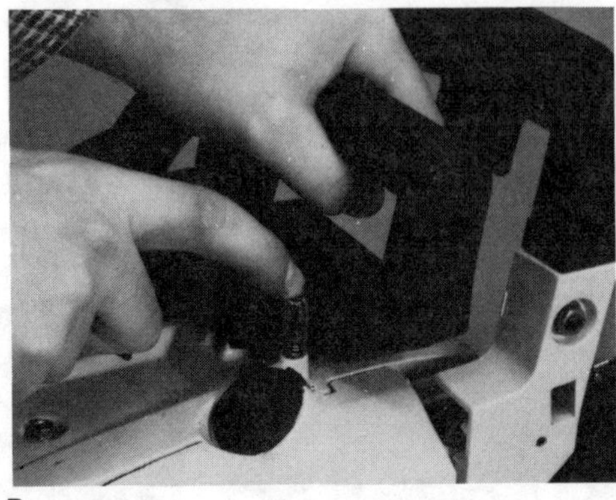

B

Fig. 2-7: (A) Clean up any gasoline spills before starting the saw. (B) Check the manual oiler to be sure the guide bar can be lubricated.

To Start

Starting of a gasoline engine is a key moment in the operation of your chain saw. To accomplish it, proceed as follows:

1. Place the saw on bare ground or another firm, flat surface. (Never start a gasoline chain saw in a closed room; it should be done outdoors.) Make sure the chain and bar do not touch anything.
2. Move the ignition/stop switch to the ON position (Fig. 2-8A). If your saw is equipped with a decompression valve or compression release, move it to the ON or START position. As mentioned in Chapter 1, this control releases the pressure against the piston and makes it easier to start the chain saw.
3. Pull the choke knob out (cold engine only). Most modern chain saws are equipped with a throttle latch button or lever near the trigger. For instance, to set the latch in the model shown in Fig. 2-8B, depress the trigger with the palm of your hand, squeeze the throttle, and lock the throttle latch by pulling the knob up. On some saws, the latch will automatically lock the trigger in a half-throttle position. Others with a trigger interlock system require that you must use your grip to simultaneously depress both the safety catch on the top and the trigger. Then, the throttle can be set in a partially OPEN position with the throttle latch.
4. When starting a standard-size chain saw with a rear handle, put the toe of your work boot in the handle and press down, stepping on the handle (Fig. 2-8C).

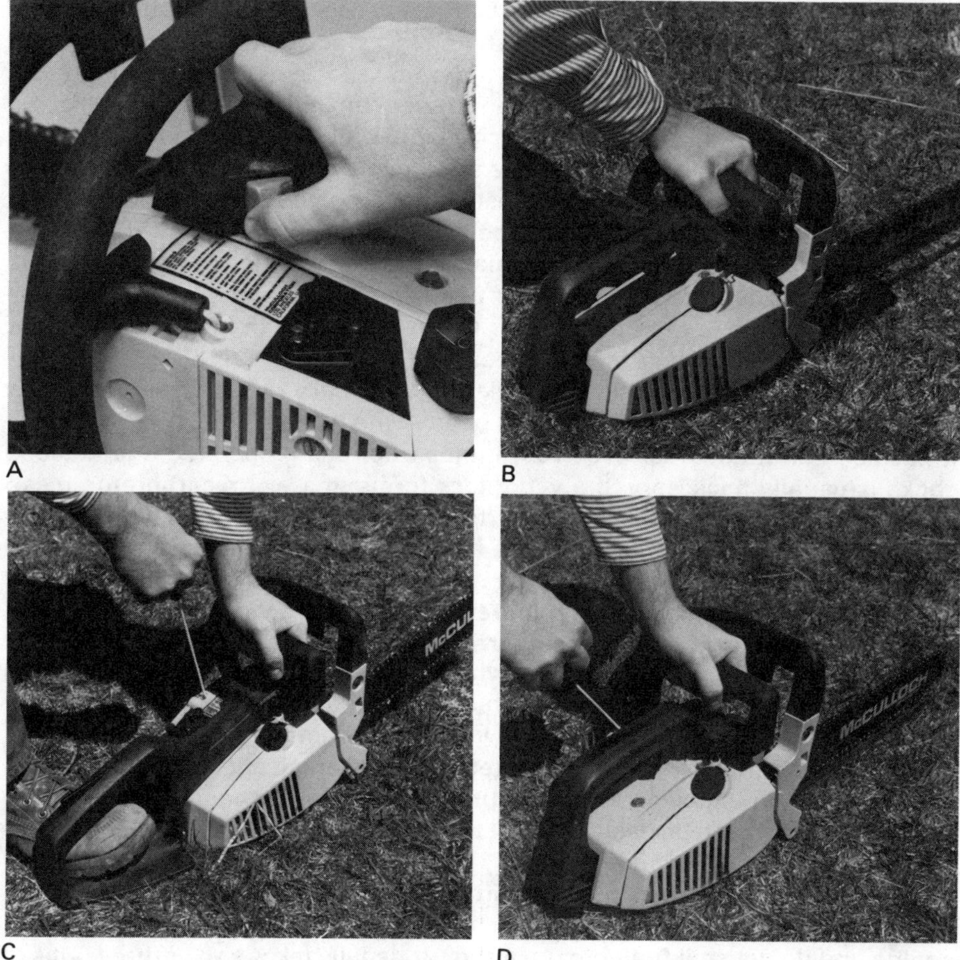

Fig. 2-8: Method of starting a chain saw.

To start a smaller saw, hold the front handle down firmly with the left hand. The thumb should be wrapped around the underside of the handle and the other fingers curved around the top (Fig. 2-8D).

5. Grasp the starter rope handle with your right hand. Be sure you have firm footing and balance. Then, pull the starter cord out slowly until you feel the starter engage. Once this occurs, make a smooth, rapid, and short pull on the starter cord to give a fast cranking spin to the engine. (Do not pull the cord to the very end or you may damage the starter.) Allow the starter rope to rewind slowly. Never let the starter rope snap back from the extended position. Also, do not wrap the starter cord around your hand.

6. Repeat the cranking action until the engine fires. Normally, an engine that has not been operated for some time requires three to five cranks just to prime with fuel. In cold weather, additional cranking may be necessary for initial prime. On the other hand, a recently operated engine will usually start up on the first or second pull. Also, a recently run chain saw will usually start with both the choke

and throttle lever in the OFF position. In freezing cold weather when the saw is not to be used right away, choke the engine to a stop, instead of using the ignition/stop switch. This leaves fuel in the engine for extra cold-starting ease.

7. If the engine fires but does not continue to run, push the choke knob down about halfway before continuing with cranking. When it starts and runs, keep it running at half-choke long enough to warm up the engine, then push the choke knob all the way in (OFF position). Most engines which have been fired several times at full choke will usually start better at half-choke.

8. Squeeze the throttle slightly to release the throttle latch button so that the engine does not overspeed but yet idles fast enough for warm-up. Do not throttle the engine to high speeds during this warm-up period. In fact, never run the engine at full throttle unless you are cutting wood.

When restarting, as mentioned earlier, it is normally unnecessary to choke a warm engine. However, if the saw has been in the hot sun or in a car trunk, or if it has been shut down for over 10 minutes after being operated, the use of a choke is usually necessary. If a vapor lock forms in a warm carburetor, it can usually be cleared out and the saw started as follows: Crank the saw alternately at full and half-choke until the engine fires. Then, operate at half-choke when the engine starts and allow it to run for no more than 30 seconds before pushing the choke knob all the way in. If required, repeat the procedure until the carburetor clears itself and the engine operates normally.

A newly manufactured saw or one which has been in storage (see Chapter 3) may sometimes be difficult to start. This is because for shipping purposes one of the manufacturing processes removes all fuel from the fuel tank, fuel lines, and carburetor after the engine is tested. Proper storage and long storage periods also result in removing or evaporating all fuel from the engine. Under these circumstances, it can be easier to start the engine in the following manner. Remove the air filter cover and air filter. Prime the engine by injecting about half a teaspoon of the proper fuel mixture through the carburetor air intake (Fig. 2-9), using an oil can filled with the proper fuel mixture. Take care not to flood the engine and do not spill fuel into the airbox. It usually takes two or three pulls of the starter rope to draw the fuel into the combustion chamber and start the engine. It may be necessary to start the engine two or three times in this manner

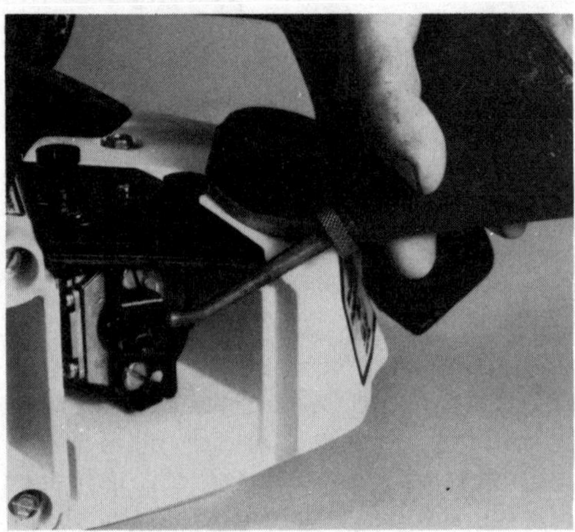

Fig. 2-9: Injecting fuel mixture through the carburetor air intake in a new engine or one that has been in storage for a period of time.

before the engine will run on its own fuel system. As soon as the engine is running on its own fuel system, stop the engine and replace the air filter and air filter cover. Never do any cutting with the air filter and air filter cover off the engine. Keep in mind, however, **not** to use this method for regular starting.

To Stop

When you wish to stop a gasoline chain saw, place the saw on a clear, firm, and flat surface. Then, pull the starter handle out slowly about 6 inches (15.2 cm) and move the ignition/stop switch to the STOP position (Fig. 2-10). This stopping procedure should be followed under *normal* circumstances in order to prevent unnecessary wear of the starting mechanism. Of course, when it is necessary to stop the saw immediately, simply move the ignition/stop switch to the STOP position.

Fig. 2-10: Method of stopping a chain saw.

Carburetor Adjustment

If your saw does not start properly or the engine does not run as you feel it should, chances are that the carburetor needs adjustment. Since chain saw carburetors are adjustable in different ways, it is also wise to follow your owner's manual for exact adjustment instructions. However, the following procedure for a typical saw carburetor will give some idea of how these critical adjustments are made. Keep in mind that if done carelessly, these adjustments can damage the carburetor and engine. Also, before performing them, make sure the air filter is clean. Very often a dirty air filter will make the engine operate as though the carburetor needed adjustment.

1. Carefully turn the low and high speed mixture needles clockwise (Fig. 2-11) until resistance is felt. Do not turn the needles in too tightly or you can damage the needle tips and their seats. Then, open (turn counterclockwise) each needle one turn.

2. Start the engine and let it warm up at low speed. If the engine will not idle without stopping, turn the idle speed screw clockwise until it does.

3. Accelerate the engine several times, adjusting the low speed mixture needle to obtain a smooth, rapid acceleration without hesitation or falter. If the

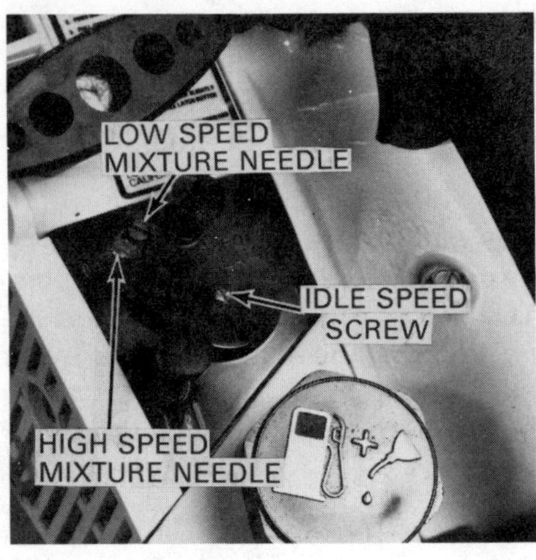

Fig. 2-11: Location of typical carburetor adjustment screw.

needle is turned in too far, the engine will hesitate or falter when accelerated. If the needle is turned out too far, the engine will run rough and smoke heavily when accelerated.

4. Adjust the high speed needle for best power under load. Do not judge by the sound; judge by the way the saw cuts. Final position of the high speed needle will usually be about one turn open.

5. Check idle operation again. It may be necessary to readjust slightly for smooth idle and acceleration. Remember that engine performance is determined by the cutting speed and ease of operation under load. Therefore, do not adjust the carburetor for maximum sound level as this is likely to result in a lean condition which can cause engine damage.

As simple as these adjustments are, it is just as simple to do something wrong; and once you have gotten the carburetor adjustment fouled up, you may spend more time trying to rectify your mistake than you will spend cutting wood.

Chain Brake Operation

If your chain saw is equipped with a chain brake (see Chapter 1), the *possibility* of injury due to kickback is greatly reduced. The brake is actuated if pressure is applied against the brake lever when, as in the event of kickback, the operator's hand strikes the lever. When the brake is actuated, chain movement stops abruptly. Remember, however, that the purpose of the chain brake is to reduce the possibility of injury due to kickback, but it cannot provide the measure of protection intended if the saw is operated carelessly.

As described in Chapter 1, the chain brake on most saws is disengaged (the chain can move) when the brake lever is pulled back and locked. The chain brake is engaged (the chain is stopped) when the brake lever is in the forward position. When the brake lever has been tripped, the chain stops. Immediately release the throttle trigger to prevent damage to the engine or clutch. If the chain brake has been actuated and the engine is idling, grasp the brake lever firmly and pull back to the locked position while controlling the saw with a hand grasping the rear handle. Be careful not to squeeze the throttle trigger. **Note:** When starting or operating a saw, the chain brake should not be engaged. Do not allow the engine to idle for *long* periods of time when the brake is engaged, as this tends to build up heat in the sprocket bearing. Never hold the saw by the chain brake lever.

Before cutting with your saw, test the chain brake as follows:

1. Place the saw on a clear, firm, and flat surface and then start the engine as previously described in this chapter.
2. Grasp the rear handle firmly with the right hand (Fig. 2-12A) and hold the front handle (not the chain brake lever) firmly with the left hand.
3. Squeeze the throttle trigger so that the chain begins to move, then activate (push forward) the chain brake lever (Fig. 2-12B). Do this very slowly and deliberately. Be careful to keep the chain from touching any surface; do not allow the saw to tip forward.
4. The chain should stop abruptly. When it does, release the throttle trigger immediately. If the chain does *not* stop, turn off the engine and check to be sure that the chain brake is properly installed. If the installation is correct, take the saw to your local dealer for repair or replacement of the chain brake assembly.

The chain brake lever/handguard provides the best protection against kickback when the saw is held at the top of the front handle (Fig. 2-12C). The wraparound chain brake lever will also act as a handguard if the saw is being held at any point on the front handle (Fig. 2-12D).

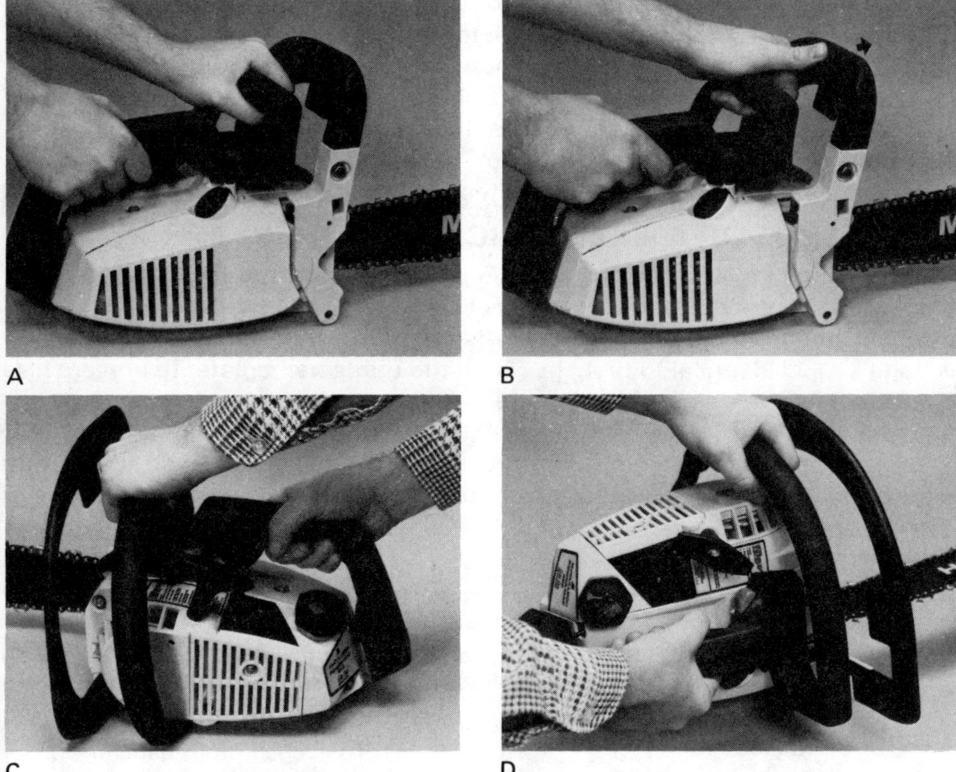

Fig. 2-12: Checking the operation of a chain brake.

A

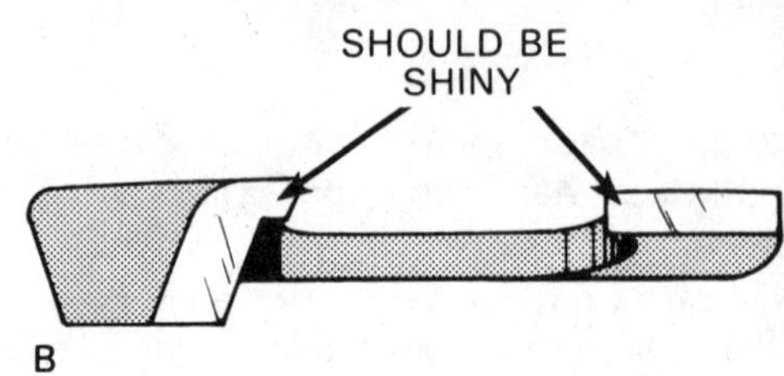

B

Fig. 2-13: Checking the operation of an automatic sharpener.

Automatic Sharpener Operation

If your chain saw is equipped with an automatic sharpening assembly, it is essential that the chain is on the bar before using the device. Attempting to operate an automatic sharpening system with a loose chain can damage the sharpening stone and/or the chain.

Before using a saw with an automatic sharpener, its operation should be carefully studied. To check a typical sharpening system, proceed as follows:

1. Start the engine on a clear, firm, and flat surface and allow it to warm up.
2. Grasp the rear handle firmly with the right hand and the adjusting knob with the fingers of the left hand. Keep hand and fingers away from the hot rear portion of the muffler shield.
3. While running the engine between 1/2 and 2/3 throttle (the correct engine speed for sharpening the chain), press down on the adjusting knob and turn clockwise one click at a time until you see sparks; hold down for 10 or 15 seconds (Fig. 2-13A). Then, release the knob and stop the engine.
4. If the grinding stone has been properly adjusted, the entire top edge of the cutter will be shiny. If any portion of the top edge is not shiny or does not reflect a sharpened condition, the adjusting knob must be pushed down and turned one or more clicks until the entire edge is sharpened (Fig. 2-13B). The amount of sparks which fly out during the sharpening operation is an indication of correct adjustment of the stone. A light flow of sparks indicates proper adjustment; no sparks or heavy flow of sparks indicates wrong adjustment.

OPERATION OF AN ELECTRIC CHAIN SAW

When using an electric chain saw (Fig. 2-14), plug it into the extension cord only when you are ready to cut wood, not before. Never leave the saw unless it is disconnected from the power source. Also, connect the chain saw to only an AC voltage supply identical to that shown on the unit's nameplate. To prevent disconnection of the saw's cord from the extension cord, make a knot such as the one shown in Fig. 2-15.

The extension cord employed for the electric chain saw must be specifically marked as suitable for outdoor use and of a sufficient gauge to transmit the current drawn by the saw.

EXTENSION CORDS

		Minimum Gauge Wire		
		Length of Cord		
Ampere Ratings	Volts AC	25 feet	50 feet	100 feet
5-6	120	18 gauge	16 gauge	14 gauge
6-8	120	18 gauge	16 gauge	12 gauge
8-10	120	16 gauge	14 gauge	12 gauge
10-12	120	16 gauge	14 gauge	10 gauge

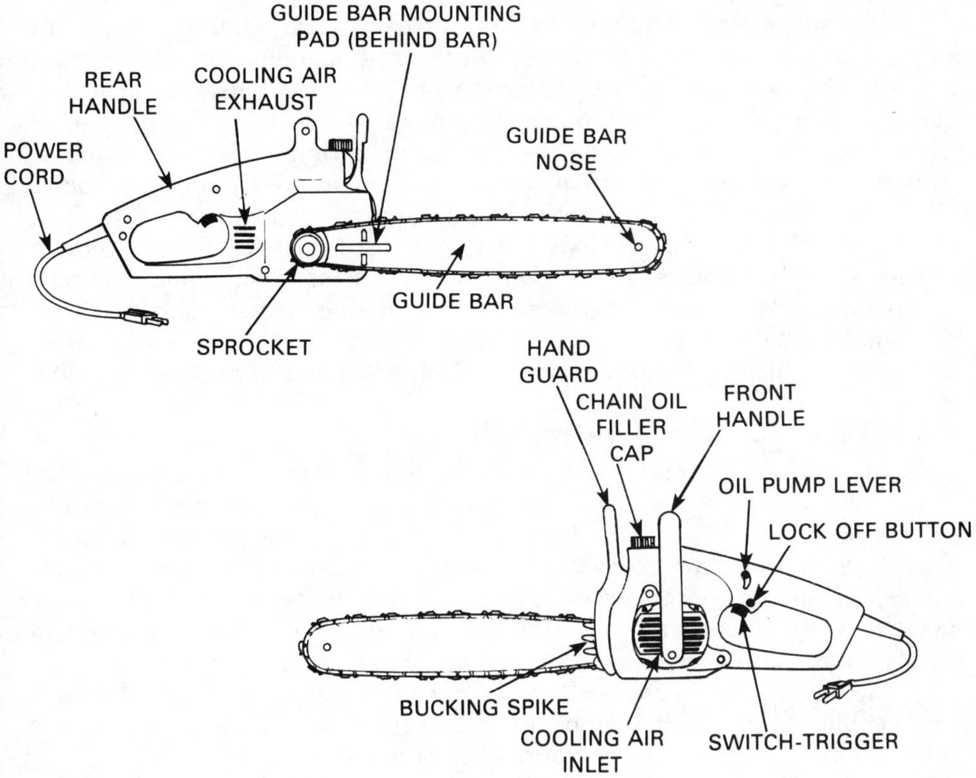

Fig. 2-14: Major parts of an electric chain saw.

Most electric chain saws are double-insulated for added safety. This means the unit is constructed throughout with two separate "layers" of electrical insulation. Chain saws built with this insulation system are not intended to be ground-

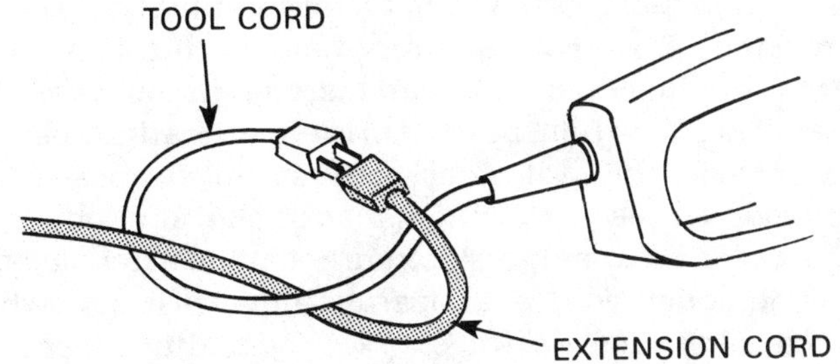

Fig. 2-15: Always knot the extension cord to the tool cord.

ed. As a result, the extension cord used with a double-insulated saw can be plugged into any conventional 120 volt AC electrical outlet without concern for maintaining a ground connection. **Note:** Double insulation does not take the place of normal safety precautions when operating an electric saw. The insulation system is for added protection against injury resulting from a possible electrical insulation failure within the saw.

The trigger, usually mounted in the rear handle, operates the switch that starts and stops the electric motor. To prevent this motor from being started accidentally, the trigger, as a rule, can only be operated if the lock-off button is depressed first. When the rear handle is gripped in a normal cutting position, the lock-off button can be pushed in by the thumb, permitting the index finger to squeeze the trigger. It is not necessary to maintain pressure on the lock-off button once the trigger has been moved from the rest position.

If the electric chain saw is equipped with a chain brake and an automatic sharpener, these accessories are operated in basically the same manner as described earlier for the gasoline models. The method of adjusting the chain is also similar. But, before using a gasoline or electric type chain saw, let us first take a look at the most important part of any chain saw cutting operation—safety.

SAFETY AND THE CHAIN SAW

Safety and good woodsmanship are both dependent on a thorough knowledge of your chain saw and the proper method of using it. As mentioned earlier, the chain saw is easy to use, but like all power tools there is a certain amount of hazard. Using the chain saw with the respect and caution demanded as far as safety precautions are concerned will considerably lessen the possibility of personal injury. However, if normal safety precautions are overlooked or completely ignored, the operator may be injured. Keep these basic rules in mind:

1. Know your chain saw. Read the owner's manual very carefully. Learn the saw's applications and limitations, as well as the specific potential hazards. Do not attempt operations beyond your capacity or experience.

2. Always wear buttoned shirt cuffs and generally close-fitting clothes when you run your chain saw, to avoid the possibility of clothing getting caught in the saw. In other words, wear the proper apparel: safety footwear, snug-fitting clothes, hard hat (in wooded areas), safety goggles or lenses, hearing protection device, and gloves.

3. Do not use any other fuel than that recommended in the owner's manual. Refuel in a safe place. Open fuel cap slowly to release any pressure which may have formed in the fuel tank. Do not start a saw where you fuel it; move at least 10 feet (3 meters) from the fueling area before starting. Do not overfill or spill fuel. If fuel has been spilled on the unit, be certain the saw has dried before starting it. Do not refuel a hot saw—allow it to cool off. Also, never smoke while fueling or operating the saw. Keep a fire extinguisher or shovel handy.

4. Before starting an electric chain saw, be sure that the extension cord and connections are in good condition. Never operate an electric saw where wet ground or damp foliage can cause electric shock. When cutting, keep the cord clear of the chain.

5. Be sure that any helpers or spectators are at a safe distance from you and the saw, and that they are not standing where they might be struck by falling branches, etc. Keep bystanders from the work area. Remember that the operation of a saw should be restricted to mature, properly instructed individuals.

6. Start your saw without help. Do not hold a saw on your leg or knee. Keep all parts of your body and clothing away from the saw chain when starting or running the engine. Before you start the engine, make sure the saw chain is not contacting anything. Never operate a chain saw when you are fatigued.

7. Hold the saw firmly with both hands when engine is running; use a firm grip with thumbs and fingers encircling the chain saw handles and watch carefully what you cut. Be sure not to let the end of the blade hit branches, stubs, stumps, or any object other than the one you are cutting. Inattention in holding or guiding the saw while cutting can cause kickback.

8. Only make cuts within the capacity of your chain saw. Stand with your weight evenly distributed on both feet for proper balance. Do not cut in awkward positions (off balance, outstretched arms, one-handed,etc.). It is recommended that you **do not** operate a saw while in a tree, on a ladder, or on any other unstable surface. If you elect to do so, be advised that these positions are extremely dangerous.

9. Clear away brush, rocks, or anything else in the working area which might hinder your movements. Use extreme caution when cutting small brush and saplings because slender material may catch the saw chain and be whipped toward you or it may pull you off balance. When cutting a limb that is under tension, be alert for springback so that you will not be struck when the tension is released.

10. Make sure that the saw chain is moving at full speed just as it enters the wood. Early revving causes the engine to race too much; late revving will cause binding and clutch slippage. Keep the cutting speed under careful control. Modern chain saws cut rapidly. It is very easy to cut too deeply or at a wrong angle. For best control, hold the bumper spikes in contact with the wood as the chain begins cutting.

11. Do not stand in line with the bar and chain. Learn to stand to one side of the cut while sawing. Never touch or try to stop a moving chain with your hand.

Fig. 2-16: Proper way of carrying a chain saw.

12. Before cutting any standing tree, prepare an escape route from it at an angle of 45 degrees in the opposite direction from the intended line of fall of the tree. Always make an undercut or notch and never cut a standing tree completely through. The "hinge" is necessary to control the direction of the fall of the tree. Use plastic or wooden wedges to control the fall of a tree or prevent binding during bucking. Do not, however, use hard metal wedges or an axe to hold cuts open. Do not fell a tree during high or changing winds.

13. Study the effects of bucking and limbing cuts on logs which may roll. Always cut and work on the uphill side of a log. Also, be sure to limb with your feet and legs in the clear and try to keep the trunk of a felled tree between you and the limb being cut. Do not limb with the nose of the guide bar; kickback can result which can prove very dangerous.

14. Never touch or let your hand come in contact with a hot muffler, spark arrester, or a spark plug wire. Never run the saw with a fuel cap loose or without a muffler, exhaust stack, or a spark arrester. Keep the screens and baffles clean.

15. Avoid prolonged operation of your chain saw and rest periodically, especially if your hands or arms start to have a loss of feeling, swell, or become difficult to move. These conditions can reduce your ability to control a saw. Also, never operate your chain saw in confined or poorly vented areas.

16. Turn off your saw when moving between cuts and before setting it down. It is best to carry or transport a shut-off saw with its bar scabbard or guard on. When this is not practical, you should carry the saw with the guide bar and saw chain to the rear and the muffler away from your body (Fig. 2-16).

17. Observe all local fire prevention regulations. Do not operate a chain saw when the weather is extremely dry and there is a fire hazard. Normally, authorities close forests to logging operations when such conditions exist. It is a good idea to stay in the cutting area for at least 15 minutes after stopping work to be sure there are no smoldering embers in the area. Put out any fires and report them, listing causes, if known, to the proper authorities.

18. Do not allow dirt, fuel, or sawdust to build up on the engine or outside of the saw. Keep all screws and fasteners tight. Never operate a chain saw that is damaged, improperly adjusted, or is not completely and securely assembled. Be sure that the saw chain stops moving when the throttle control trigger is released and the saw returns to idle. Keep the handles dry, clean, and free of oil or fuel mixture.

19. Never operate a saw with a loose chain. Check the chain tension frequently. Always stop the engine when adjusting the chain tension. Also, make sure that the chain and bar are receiving enough oil.

20. Keep the chain sharp. Touch up the chain teeth every couple of hours or whenever the sawing starts producing sawdust rather than chips of uniform size. It is important to keep in mind that in addition to tiring you, a dull chain can lead to excessive pressure on the saw bar and accidents. But, when you are sharpening or adjusting the blade, wear gloves or take extra precautions not to draw your finger across a saw tooth. Both the sharpness of the teeth and their shape make them inflict cuts easily.

Operating Your Chain Saw 3

The modern chain saw is a simple tool to operate, but like any power tool, it can be dangerous. For this reason, you must approach the operating of your chain saw with attentiveness and respect. According to a recent Consumer Products Safety survey, two of every three accidents to casual operators and helpers are **caused by inadvertent contact with the moving chain.** A careless move, such as reaching across or holding the work near the moving chain, or loss of footing and subsequent loss of saw control, account for many accidents.

OPERATION OF A CHAIN SAW

To become familiar with a new chain saw, it is a good idea to practice holding it and simulating a work stance without the machine running. Once you feel comfortable handling the saw, start the engine and cut some wood.

Holding the Saw. Wear nonslip gloves for maximum grip and protection. Grasp the front handle bar firmly with the left hand so that your fingers wrap around it, keeping the handle bar diameter in the webbing between your index finger and thumb (Fig. 3-1). Grasping the handle bar in this way gives you maximum control of the saw and reduces the chances of your hand slipping into the moving chain. Your right hand should wrap around the throttle control handle in such a manner as to provide good saw balance. Always keep both hands on the saw. Never shift hand positions or cross arms for easing strain or for better reach. If your arms tire, stop the saw and rest for a while.

Fig. 3-1: Proper way to hold a chain saw and position oneself when cutting.

Stance. Clear away brush, rocks, or anything else in the working area which might hinder your movements. Be sure to have safe, sure footing, and always keep your weight as equally balanced as possible on both feet. Hold the saw so that the chain is not in line with your body. Always cut with your left arm extended as straight as possible. Since you will be exerting downward pressure to cut, guard against the loss of balance by being ready to hold up on the saw as it cuts through the wood.

Cutting Wood

The most desirable way to hold a log while cutting it into lengths is to use a sawbuck (see Chapter 3). When this is not possible, the log should be raised and supported by the limbs or logs. But, be sure that it is *well* supported. Then, start the chain saw as detailed in Chapter 2. After it is warmed and idling smoothly, you are ready to cut, keeping the following points in mind:

1. Holding the saw firmly in both hands and with the engine idling, bring the cutting unit up above the log, with the nose of the guide bar pointing slightly upward. Slowly lower the power unit portion of the saw so that the bumper spikes grab into the wood and act as a pivot; the chain should not touch the wood. If the saw has a manual oiler, lubricate the chain and bar. Then, squeeze the throttle trigger so that the engine is going at top speed (full throttle) as the chain touches the wood. Never run the engine slowly at the start or during the cut. Cutting at partial speed will allow the clutch to slip and burn, wearing it out early or giving a quick glaze on the clutch friction surfaces, which leads to even more slipping and burning.
2. Guide the saw, without forcing it, through the cut. Use only enough pressure to keep the chain cutting full wood chips. In other words, let the saw do most of the work.
3. Always cut as close to the engine end of the guide bar as possible. Also, employ the saw bumper spike when practical to act as a pivot during a cut. While small logs can usually be cut straight through (Fig. 3-2), larger ones are best sawn using the bumper spikes as a pivot. While the saw is cutting, be sure the chain and bar are being lubricated. A manual oiler should be pumped every 15 to 20 seconds during the cut.
4. Do not twist the guide bar, and **make sure that the nose of the bar does not touch anything.** Never allow a running saw to contact the ground or metal; one such contact can dull the chain more than cutting dozens of trees. Also, avoid knots, if possible.
5. To maintain complete control of the saw when nearing the end of a cut, ease up on the cutting pressure without relaxing your grip on the handles. Be ready to release the throttle trigger the instant that the chain breaks through the wood. Do not permit the saw to run at full throttle without a cutting load.
6. When cutting a log on a slope, always stand on firm ground, uphill and away from the area where the log might roll. Make sure no one is below where you are working.
7. To prevent the two sections of a log from coming together and binding or pinching the chain or guide bar when the cut is nearly completed, the cut must be made to relieve any stress. As shown in Fig. 3-3A, make a cut one-third of the way through and underneath the log using the top portion of the guide bar. Then, finish the cut from the top by sawing downward into the first cut using the bot-

A
PULL UP
BUMPER SPIKE
B

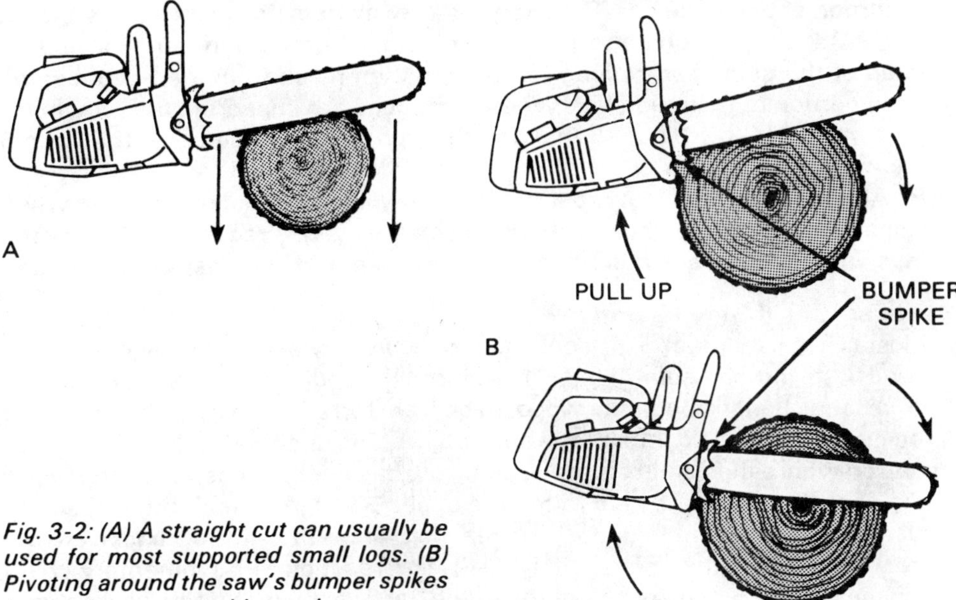

Fig. 3-2: (A) A straight cut can usually be used for most supported small logs. (B) Pivoting around the saw's bumper spikes is best for supported larger logs.

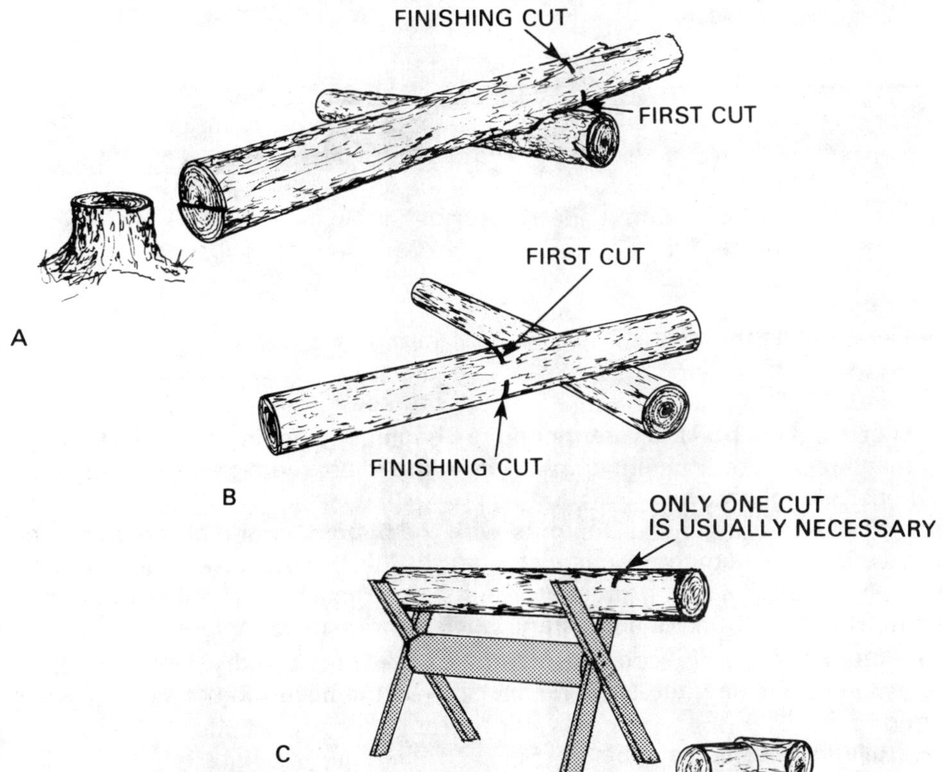

FINISHING CUT
FIRST CUT
A
FIRST CUT
FINISHING CUT
B
ONLY ONE CUT IS USUALLY NECESSARY
C

Fig. 3-3: Methods of cutting logs.

tom portion of the guide bar. The log will fall away from the guide bar. As shown in Fig. 3-3B, cut through one-third of the distance from the top using the bottom portion of the guide bar (pulling chain), and then finish from the bottom using the top portion of the guide bar. When small logs are supported on a sawbuck, as shown in Fig. 3-3C, cut all the way through from the top using the bottom portion of the guide bar.

8. Although the chain saw does most of the work, you must remain alert when using it. Cutting with a chain saw when you are overly tired is one of the worst things you can do. Take a break anytime you feel the slightest bit of fatigue.

Avoiding Chain Saw Hazards

Most chain saw hazards are caused by *momentary* chain stoppage—usually caused by its hitting a solid object. This causes the engine torque, which normally drives the chain through the wood, to be transferred to the guide bar, creating a reaction around the center of the solid object. The direction of the reaction depends on where the contact is made along the bar. For instance, when the upper chain near the nose of the bar (often the upper 90-degree quadrant) hits an obstruction or catches in the wood, the reaction forces the saw in a backward arc or rotation toward the operator (Fig. 3-4). The reaction of a momentary chain stoppage along the top portion of the guide bar is to push the saw back toward

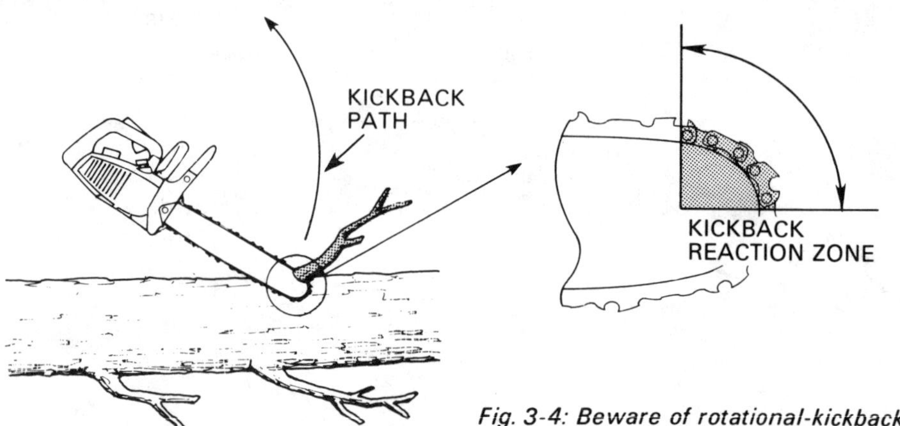

Fig. 3-4: Beware of rotational-kickback.

the operator (Fig. 3-5A). As mentioned in Chapter 1, pinching-kickback (a pushing reaction) and rotational-kickback (a backward arc reaction) are major chain saw operational hazards.

When overbucking or making cuts with the bottom portion of the guide bar, the reaction to a momentary chain stoppage is felt as a pull away from the operator (Fig. 3-5B). The best protection against pull reaction, as well as rotational- and pinching-kickback, is a constant lookout for such conditions as:

- Abrupt change of wood characteristics (i.e., green to dry, knots, etc.).
- Running the saw too slowly, especially at the beginning of a cut or when boring.
- Buildup of damp sawdust.
- A twig caught in the chain and jamming against the work.
- A branch or obstruction on the opposite side.

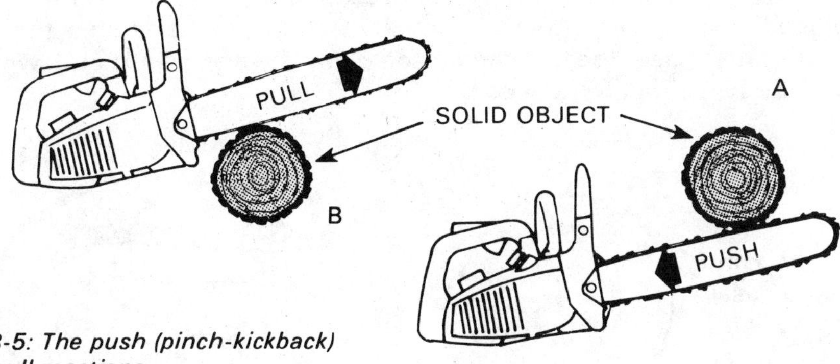

Fig. 3-5: The push (pinch-kickback) and pull reactions.

- Twisting of the saw so that the cutters grab the wood.
- Hitting the nose of the guide bar against a solid object.
- Closing or pinching of the chain kerf.
- A chain that does not have enough tension, is dull, or has too low a depth gauge setting.

Maintaining a good balance is of the utmost importance when resisting any pulling, pushing, or rotational forces. Make sure that your stance is correct, with the body weight as evenly distributed on both feet as possible.

There are other chain saw hazards to guard against. For instance, a broken chain can be dangerous. However, if you position yourself so that no part of your body is in line with the chain, chances are very good that if the chain should break, it will run off the saw and onto the ground. To guard against the rare times when a broken chain will occur, most manufacturers have provided such safety devices as chain-catching pins and right-hand guards (see Chapter 1).

The chances of any of the various chain saw hazards occurring can be greatly reduced by following the safety rules given in Chapter 2 and by wearing the woodcutting attire described in Chapter 1. The latter is most important when working in the woods.

Boring With a Chain Saw

A bore- or plunge-cut is one in which the nose of the guide bar is used to start and continue the cut through the wood. Because of the constant danger of rotational kickback, or a push reaction, boring cuts should not be attempted by any operator who is not certain he/she has the strength and experience to evaluate the risk involved and is able to control the saw. Boring should be used only when there is no other way of making the necessary cut. For instance, it may be necessary to bore when some obstruction—a rock, another log or a tree, or the ground—prevents you from placing the bottom portion of the guide bar across the wood, keeps you from continuing through with a bucking cut, or prevents you from getting underneath the log to relieve stresses with an underbuck. Boring is also necessary when performing such log carpentry tasks as cutting blind holes in fenceposts (see Chapter 7) and when making cutouts for log cabin windows. **But when making any boring cuts, always be on guard against kickback.**

To minimize danger of kickback, begin with an angular cut as far back on the nose of the guide bar (Fig. 3-6) as possible. When this cut has become deep enough to serve as a guide, exert sufficient downward pressure to bring the bar slowly into line for boring either through the log or up to the depth of the guide bar. In the latter case, the cut can be completed by an upward or downward swing of the bar through the wood.

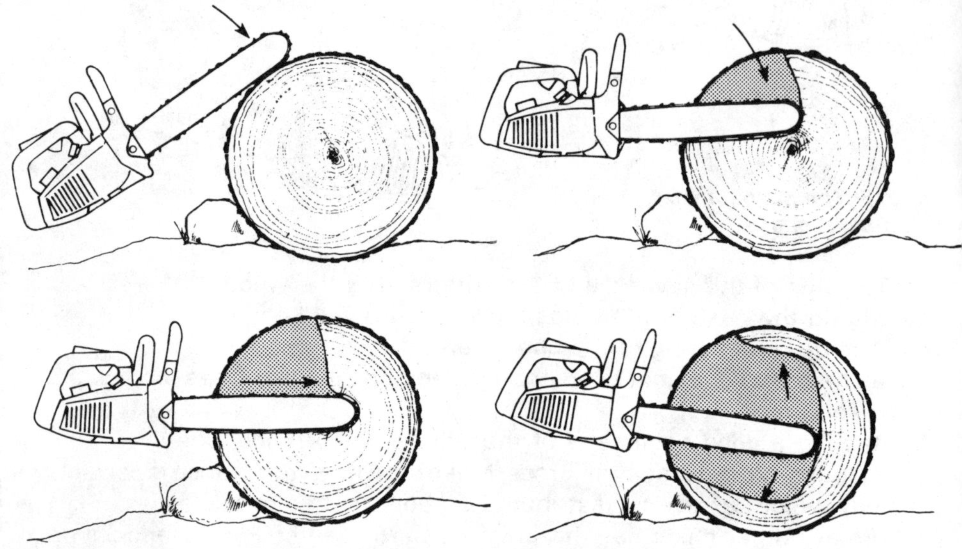

Fig. 3-6: Steps in making a boring cut. This cut was necessary because of a rock obstruction which would not permit a normal cutting procedure. Remember that boring is a dangerous cut and should be employed only as a last resort.

Sawbucks

Since the chain saw must be held with two hands, one of the most difficult parts of using it to cut wood—especially if you work alone—is getting the logs to hold still. As stated earlier in the chapter, the best way to hold a log in place is to use a sawbuck. In addition, it saves your back, since the wood is at a comfortable sawing level, and it saves your chain, since cutting wood directly on the ground is the easiest way to dull it.

As shown in Fig. 3-7, sawbucks can be light logs, dimensional lumber, or a combination of both. To build the all-log version, cut a 4-inch (10.2 cm) diameter log into two 2-foot (61 cm) pieces and four 3-foot (91.4 cm) pieces. (The length of the latter pieces may be varied to suit your best cutting height.) Assemble the four longer pieces into a pair of X's, leaving about 1 foot (30.5 cm) above the cross points. Use lag screws, nuts and bolts, or long spikes to hold the pieces together. Then, adjust the two X pieces to exactly 90 degrees and fasten them together using the short log pieces, as shown in Fig. 3-7A.

The two-legged sawbuck shown in Fig. 3-8 is handy for cutting long logs into short lengths. If fastened with a 1/2-inch (1.3 cm) bolt and a wingnut or lashed together with rawhide, it can easily be collapsed for transporting or storing. To use this sawbuck, lift one end of the log to be cut and put the X under it; the log

Fig. 3-7: Three types of sawbucks.

Fig. 3-8: A two-legged sawbuck.

will act as the third leg in a typical tripod fashion. Cut on the free side of the sawbuck and avoid hitting it with any portion of the saw. As you make successive cuts, keep lifting the end of the log and moving the two-legged sawbuck back.

OPERATIONAL ADJUSTMENTS

When using a chain saw at home or in the woods, a few adjustments are needed to keep it operating smoothly and efficiently. Perhaps the engine stalls while idling, runs too rapidly, or speeds up slowly. These situations are usually caused by carburetor maladjustment and can be corrected by adjusting the carburetor as described in the owner's manual or in Chapter 2. Of course, before making any carburetor adjustment, make sure the air filter and muffler are not clogged by dirt and debris. When cleaning the muffler, which is usually a simple task, do not attempt to do it if the saw has just been running, because mufflers do get *extremely* hot. If your saw is equipped with a spark arrester, keep in mind that it must be cleaned daily.

If the saw still is not running well, check the fuel filter. But, when removing the fuel cap, make sure that the entire top or cover plate is perfectly clean and free of all dirt, wood chips, and so on. Then, with the cap removed, the fuel filter can be

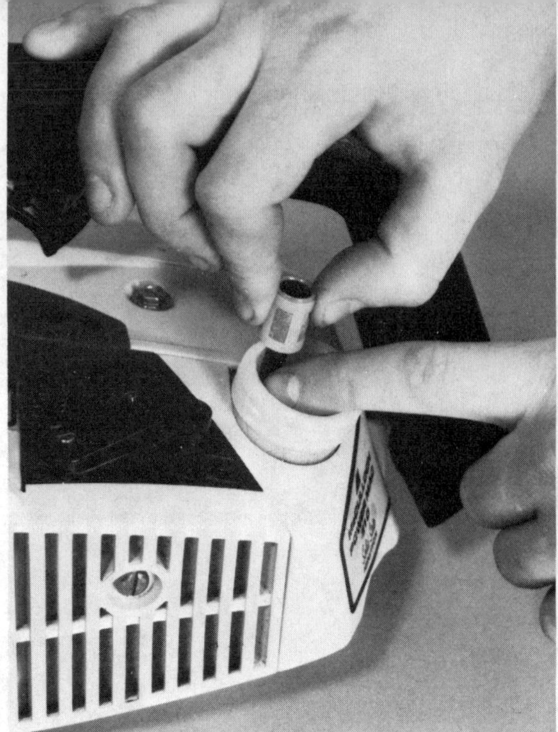

Fig. 3-9: Inspecting the fuel filter.

located by fishing around in the fuel tank with your finger or a piece of hooked wire and gently pulling the fuel line partly out of the fuel-filler port (Fig. 3-9), which is where the fuel is poured during refueling. The filter usually consists of a felt filter element or very fine wire mesh on the flared tip of the fuel line, and it should be immediately obvious if it is blocked by debris.

If the engine does not run smoothly or if it is difficult to start, chances are that the spark plug is at fault. To check a spark plug, proceed as described in Chapter 10. If defective, replace.

A complete chain saw engine troubleshooting guide can be found in Chapter 10.

Chain Adjustments

Check the chain tension before starting the saw and at frequent intervals thereafter, particularly during the first 4 to 6 hours of use. A new chain will stretch during this period, and the tension can become dangerously loose.

The adjustment procedure described in Chapter 2 outlines an important consideration when adjusting the tension of a typical chain saw. For specific information on this operation of your saw, check the owner's manual. It is best to lubricate the chain well and let it cool for several minutes before making an adjustment. A warm chain will always sag or hang down from the guide bar. This is normal; leave it alone unless the chain sags so far that the chain center links are out of the guide bar groove. If this is the case, it will be necessary to retension the warm chain. Of course, a chain that is too loose when it is cold can expand enough to permit it to jump off the bar and sprocket when it gets hot.

Proper chain tension (Fig. 3-10), as previously mentioned, is with the bottom of the tie straps and cutters just touching the bar rails of the bottom of the bar. You should be able to easily pull the chain around the bar by hand. On sprocket-nose bars, the chain must be slightly tighter. When handling any chain, always wear gloves.

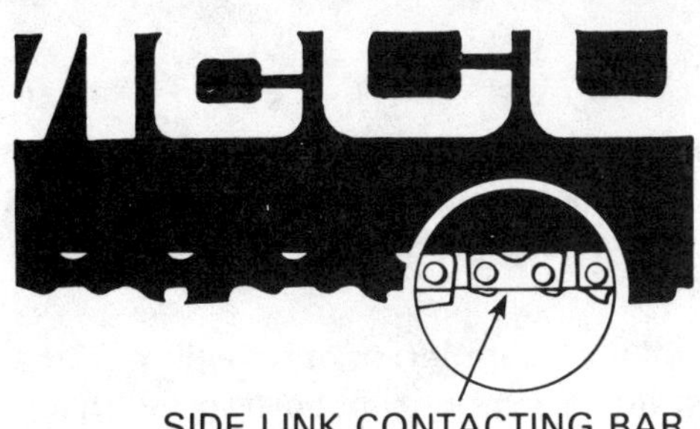

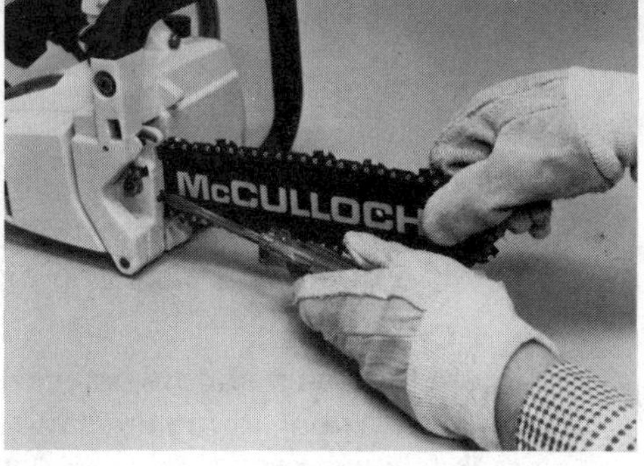

Fig. 3-10: (A) When the chain is cold, the chain side links should touch the bar rails; and (B) the chain can be pulled along the bar without binding. If the drive links are close to or coming out of the bar groove (C), the chain needs adjustment. (D) Adjust the tension of the warm chain to a maximum droop of about 1/8 inch.

An under-oiled chain will be hot and stiff and will frequently kink up, becoming very tight on the guide bar. Should this occur, check the operation of the automatic and/or manual oilers. If either are not operating properly, check the oil supply and the condition of the pick-up screen in the chain oil tank. If the oil supply is adequate and the screen is clean, allow the chain and guide bar to cool, and then remove them from the engine housing. Clean out the chain oil slot on the guide mounting pad. After cleaning the chain and guide bar, remount them on the engine and adjust the chain to the proper tension. Start the engine and operate the manual oiler. After approximately 30 seconds, shut off the engine and check for oil on the chain. If it does not appear moist with oil, the oil pump or hoses are probably faulty and should be repaired by your nearest authorized service dealer.

The chain's cutters may occasionally require touch-up sharpening during a cutting project. This is accomplished as detailed in Chapter 9. The operation of an automatic sharpener is covered in Chapter 2.

Breaking In a New Engine

Breaking in a new chain saw engine is very important. Run your engine for its first few minutes at one-third throttle. Increase speed to about half-throttle and run for a few minutes longer. Cut a few limbs or small logs at first. Check chain tension frequently and use the manual oiler button often.

It is advisable to use a slightly richer fuel mixture during the break-in period.

Turn the high speed mixture needle about one-eighth turn counterclockwise from the normal preliminary starting position. After about an hour's operation, turn the adjusted needle back one-eighth turn clockwise.

Storing a Chain Saw

Ideally, a chain saw should be operated for a short period of time (5 minutes) every 30 days. When storing the saw for short periods or transporting it with fuel in the tank, always keep the saw level and with the fuel cap up to avoid leakage from the tank or cap vent. Never store a chain saw for over 30 days without performing the following procedures.

1. Drain the fuel tank in a safe area (Fig. 3-11A).
2. Start the saw and run at idle speed until the engine stops. This will remove most of the fuel from the fuel system.
3. Remove the spark plug with a spark plug wrench and pour a teaspoonful of oil through the spark plug hole into the combustion chamber (Fig. 3-11B). Pull the starter rope slowly several times to distribute the oil throughout the engine. Replace the spark plug tightly.
4. Remove and clean the bar and chain (use gloves when handling chain).
5. Store the chain in a container, such as a coffee can, filled with enough oil to cover the chain. Then, cover the container with a tight lid.
6. Apply a heavy film of oil over the entire bar including the groove for the chain. Cover with heavy paper, cloth, or plastic.
7. Clean the outside surfaces of the saw.
8. Place a light, protective cloth or plastic covering over the saw, and store the saw and bar in a dry place. **Caution:** The covering should be loose to allow for proper ventilation. Always store away from possible sources of ignition such as furnaces, heaters, etc.

Removal From Storage. When putting a chain saw back into service, remove the spark plug with a spark plug wrench. Pull the starter rope briskly to clear the cylinder of excess oil. Clean and gap the spark plug or install a new spark plug. Fill the fuel tank with the correct fuel mixture and fill the chain oil tank with a good chain, bar, and sprocket oil. For hints on easy starting of an engine that has been in storage for a period of time, see Chapter 2.

A

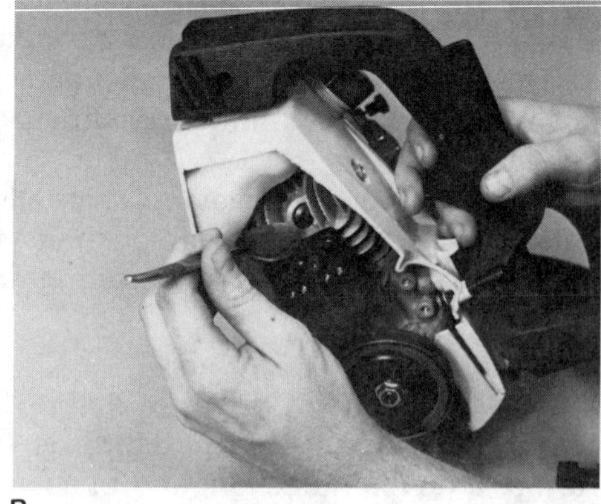

B

Fig. 3-11: Putting a chain saw in storage.

Tree Limbing, Bucking, and Felling 4

Felling, limbing, and bucking are the operations that are involved in bringing a standing tree to useable logs. That is, felling (or falling) is cutting down a tree; limbing is the removing of the branches from a felled tree; and bucking is the cutting of a tree into logs of desired length.

Because felling requires the most chain saw skill and experience, it is usually wise for the inexperienced woodsman to practice limbing and bucking on downed trees before attempting to fell a tree himself. For this reason, limbing and bucking will be covered first in this chapter before discussing felling. The basic cutting and safety tips given in Chapters 2 and 3, of course, hold true whenever performing limbing, bucking, or felling.

LIMBING

Limbing a downed tree is not a difficult task, especially if it is done with a lightweight chain saw with a short bar. However, there are precautions that *must* be taken. For instance, before starting to limb up a felled or downed tree, check to be sure that some of the limbs are not holding the tree from rolling. Also, check overhead for broken limbs or chunks that may fall at any time.

It is best to start at the butt of the tree and work towards the top so that the branches will be pointing away from you while you are working. Always stay on the uphill side if there is a chance the tree may roll or shift. Make sure you have good footing and a well-balanced stance. Clear limbs from your working area as you progress. For the most part, limbs are cut with the lower portion of the bar, so beware of potential kickback. On limbs that are standing out free from the trunk, cut the bottom side of the limb one-third of the way through with a pushing chain, then cut down from the top to finish the cut with a pulling chain. When a branch is supported at both ends (by the tree at one end, and the ground at the other), topcut the branch first to prevent binding. Then, finish with an undercut. A wedge undercut is generally not necessary. On larger limbs, leave some connecting wood to guide or control the limb as it is falling away, and be careful it does not fall on you. To make bucking easier under some conditions, it may be best to leave some supporting limbs uncut. These may be cut off after bucking.

When limbing, keep a firm grip on the saw with both hands. Beware of limbs under pressure; they can throw chips and cause kickback. First cut the side of the limb that is being compressed by the log's weight. Do this very carefully with the tip of the bar, and never make the cut very deep, usually about one-fourth of the limb's diameter. Then, finish the cut from the other side, expecting a sudden snap, flying debris, and possible shifting of the log.

Fig. 4-1: When limbing, it is best to keep the tree trunk between you and the guide bar (left). In cases where this is not possible (right), exercise care to make sure that you do not allow the saw to swing into your leg.

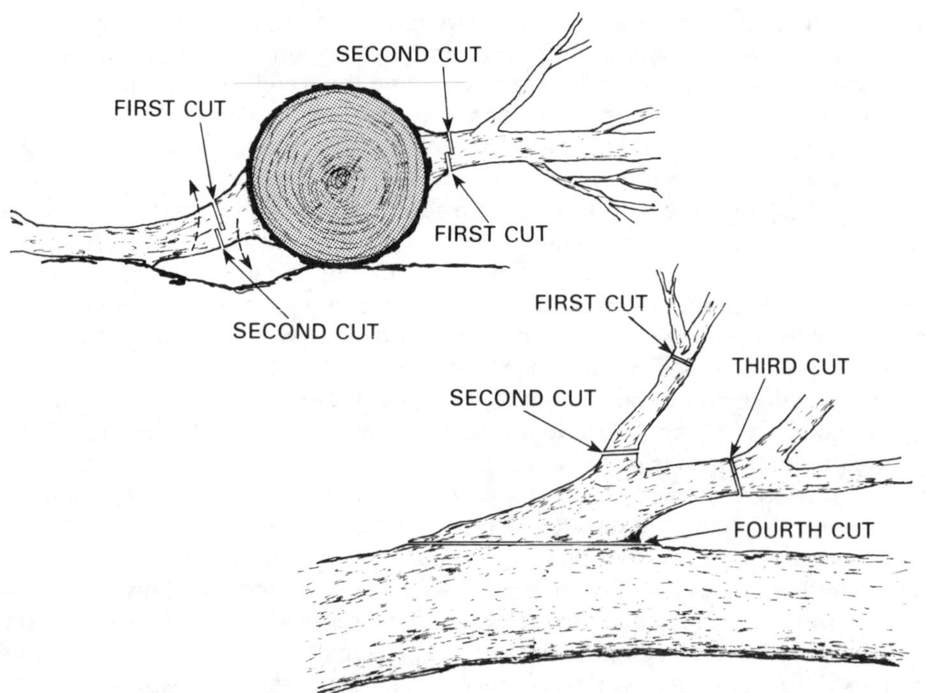

Fig. 4-2: When limbing a tree with large or complex branches, be sure to make cuts that will relieve stress.

For safety, as mentioned in Chapter 2, it is generally a good idea to stand on the opposite side from that which you are limbing (Fig. 4-1). In this manner, you use the trunk as a barrier between you and the cutting chain. If some of the limbs fall into the way of your next cut, shut the saw off and clear your work area. If it becomes necessary to limb on the same side of the trunk that you are standing, use caution and a firm grip. Do not allow the saw to swing down into your leg after completing the cut. Also, no cuts should be made while standing on the tree.

Large limbs or complex branch structures can frequently be a problem in that they may pinch the chain or split the wood if not handled correctly. It is important that you choose the proper sequence of cutting operations (Fig. 4-2) to relieve stress or tension on the cut. When cutting main branches, it may be necessary to undercut it first and finish it with a top cut. If any branch is in a bind, start with a top cut and finish with an undercut.

If your saw is equipped with a chain brake, engage it to stop the chain while clearing away cut limbs or when moving short distances. This will stop any chain movement. The engine must be stopped on saws without a chain brake.

BUCKING

A common hazard that you can run into when bucking or limbing is a sapling or bush that was bent over when the tree was felled. This is sometimes called a "spring pole" or "sidewinder," but you may call it worse than that if you unexpectedly get hit by one. When mixed with branches and other small material, you may not identify it and inadvertently cut it off. Even a small sapling, bent in this manner, can have enough force to cause a bad bruise or, even worse, throw the running saw back at you. The safest way to handle this situation, if possible, is not to cut it at all. If you feel that it should be cut, the safest method is to use an axe and cut from the compression or underside.

The same problem of stress when cutting logs, discussed in Chapter 3, should be kept in mind when bucking logs in the woods. Unless a log is blocked or supported in some way, you will seldom find one that is not subject to at least some directional force somewhere along its length. These forces must be read correctly and the cuts made in a manner that will avoid pinching and binding the saw. The wood will be under tension on one side of the log and a cut here will open up. It will be under compression on the opposite side, which will cause the cut to close and the saw to bind.

To buck a log that is on level ground and is supported along its full length with no apparent bind, make the following sequence of cuts (Fig. 4-3A). Set the bumper spikes and start the cut at the top of the log. Pivot the saw forward to make the backside cut. Stop the cut when the bar tip is still a few inches from the ground. Next, draw the saw back and drop down on the near face; then, dog in for the next cut. Always release the throttle trigger when the chain is running free and not cutting. Pivot the saw forward again as in the first cut and repeat this process until the log is nearly cut through. To finish the cut, throttle back to slow the chain and withdraw the bar until only the bottom portion of the tip remains in the cut. Move the tip back and forth across the uncut wood and continue to slow the chain speed as the cut nears completion. If there is thick bark on the log, watch for a

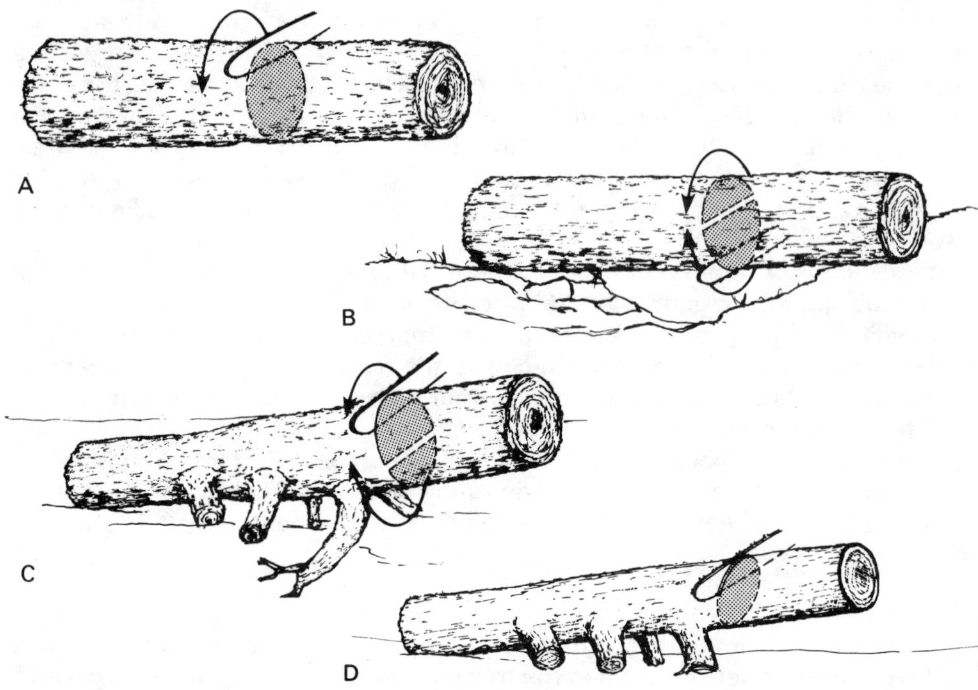

Fig. 4-3: How to buck a log under various stress situations.

color change in the sawdust that will indicate the sound wood has been cut. Release the throttle and withdraw the bar before it cuts all the way through into the ground and dulls the chain.

If a log is supported on both ends, as covered in Chapter 3, a single straight cut from the top would bind the saw, so examine the proper sequence of cuts to make. The first cut is an overbuck made through one-third the diameter of the log to avoid splintering. The second cut, an underbuck, meets the first cut and avoids pinching (Fig. 4-3B).

Until now, most of our cuts have been made with the bottom edge of the bar. This type of cut pulls the saw away from you and actually helps pull the saw into the log. When using the top portion of the bar, the chain saw will be pushed or thrusted towards you. Make sure that you have good footing and are able to stabilize yourself adequately. Be extremely alert to the possibility of a kickback. Occasionally, the cutters on the chain will bind when cutting like this, and the bar will kick up and back suddenly and severely. Be aware of this possibility, and at all times, maintain a secure hold on your saw.

When a log is supported on only one end (Fig. 4-3C), the first cut is made from the bottom up (underbuck). This cut should come up approximately one-third of the diameter of the log. As previously discussed, make sure of your footing and maintain a firm grip on the saw. Next, cut the back side of the log, and then make the final cut from the top down. By doing this, you can position yourself out of danger if the log should snap off unexpectedly. The end of the log should drop away and not pinch the bar. As a precaution against possible binding of the bar, again position your plastic or wood wedges in the cut as soon as possible.

Frequently, where only one end of the log is supported (Fig. 4-3D), a single cut from the top at a slight angle in towards the supported bottom will generally allow the unsupported end to fall away without binding.

Under stress conditions, when cutting logs that are larger than the length of the guide bar, it is usually necessary to make a number of cuts in sequence. The purpose of these cuts is to leave a break-off hinge of uncut wood. The exact location of this hinge is determined by the points of stress. For example, when the log is supported on one end (Fig. 4-4A), you will want the hinge in the lower third of the log to prevent splitting. To accomplish this, make a through cut on the far side of the log. Then, cutting from the bottom (a pushing chain), leave the upper third hinge. The third cut is an underbuck on the close side of the log, and it will place the chain saw in position for the fourth cut—an overbuck. The final cut is then back down to the topside of the hinge and through it.

When cutting a large log that is supported on both ends with a small guide bar saw, make an overbuck cut (pulling chain cut) down on the far side of the log. Then, cut down from the top to form a hinge in the upper third of the log. The next three cuts will be underbucks, as shown in Fig. 4-4B. When making the final pulling cut, be sure you have full control of the saw.

When bucking a log that is lying straight up and down the slope (Fig. 4-5), the upper section could slide down and apply end pressure, binding the bar in the cut. Here you will need to use a wedge. Tap it in deep enough to allow the saw to cut without binding. A wedge cut may also be used on a log where end pressure may result. Cut out a wedge or pie approximately two-thirds the diameter of the log, and then finish the buck.

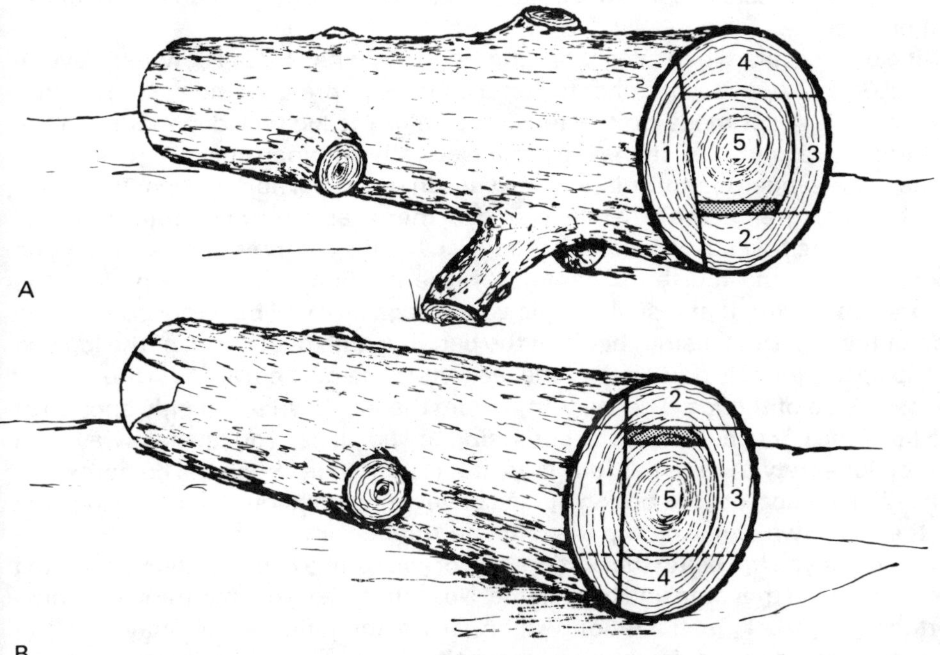

Fig. 4-4: Methods of bucking logs that are larger in diameter than the length of the guide bar. The idea is to leave a break-off hinge of uncut wood.

Fig. 4-5: Bucking a log lying straight up and down a slope.

Occasionally, you may come across a downed log that has been placed in a side bind by being wedged between trees, rocks, or stumps. If you can go around it without bucking it, do so. These logs are potentially very dangerous as it is quite difficult to predict which way the log will roll. If you have no choice but to cut the log, clear out an area for your feet and enough additional area so that you can move quickly out of the way should it break unexpectedly. Whenever possible, do your cutting from the uphill side. Occasionally, extreme bind may make it necessary for you to work on the low side. In this situation, work as close as is safe to one of the objects causing the bind, preferably a tree of 18-inch diameter (45 cm) or larger.

Side bind occurs when a log is sprung sideways when forced between several solid objects. Always remember to stand on the compression side of the log that is being cut. A cut made on the tension side of the log will, depending on the amount of pressure, cause the log to split laterally and snap outward. This is one of the more dangerous situations a sawyer can run into when bucking. The stress may be much greater than just the weight of the log as in top or bottom bind cuts. Therefore, the first cut should be a wedge cut on the compression side of the log approximately one-fourth its diameter. Make the first cut, and then place the second cut next to it at a slight angle so a wedge or V will be removed from the side of the log. Next, using the tip of the bar, bore into the bottom of the log and cut up approximately one-third of the diameter. The next cut is down the back or opposite side of the log. The last cut is from the top down using only enough of the tip of the bar to complete the cut. Using the tip places you farther away from the log for safety. Again, the four cuts are: (1) a wedge cut on the compression side; (2) a cut up from the bottom; (3) a cut down the tension side of the log; and (4) the cut down from the top to complete the bucking operation.

Wherever you are doing the cutting, one of your prime considerations is getting the wood out of that area and back home. No matter what your means of log transportation is—truck, jeep, station wagon, or tractor—this vehicle may help you pull fallen trees to a safer and more suitable limbing and bucking position. Of course, you must be careful that your vehicle is capable of handling the job and that the tree does not tumble over onto it. If the trunk is not too heavy, it can be cut into sections to split the weight, so that you can lift it with a log lifter or turn it with a peavey. If you are not making wood bolts or saw logs, the sectional cuts can be made anywhere along the trunk. Choose the areas where your saw will not bind.

FELLING

Felling of live standing trees and snags (dead trees) should begin only after a sawyer has acquired the feeling of operating a chain saw and has confidence and expertise in maintaining complete control. The more attention a sawyer can focus on the felling process, the safer the job will be. Actually, before felling any tree or snag, you must make a thorough check of many conditions and situations. Identifying the species may help to determine if the wood will be soft or brittle. Take, for example, a large pine snag. Snags such as this will always have brittle wood. The size in this instance would be important. Is your saw large enough to effectively handle such a large felling job? Remember that while all felling can be dangerous, the dangers and complications increase as the tree's size increases. Also, a large tree means more limbing and bucking, so more consideration must be given to where it is going to fall and how you are going to handle it once it is down. After a tree is lying in its bed is no time to wish you had put it down several degrees in another direction. Think out every step first, not only for the felling, but also for the limbing, bucking, and final wood removal. The bigger the tree, the more carefully you must plan. When you hang up a small tree, it is a problem; hang up a big one and you have got *big* trouble.

Before Felling a Tree

The first step in any felling job is to remove or treat any hazards in the work area. Broken chunks of wood and loose rocks should be removed from the base of the tree so you will not trip if you have to step back quickly from the falling tree. If there is snow on the ground, it should be tramped down or cleared away to assure good footing. Brush and small trees should be removed along with any lower branches that may get in the way.

When limbing a standing tree for felling, a firm grip and absolute control of the saw must be maintained. Be cautious of kickback, do not let the saw swing down into you, and never cut higher than your shoulder or head. On larger limbs, make a small undercut on the bottom side of the limb. Next, cut the limb from the top about 1 inch (2.5 cm) farther out. This will prevent the limb from peeling the bark. On small limbs, one single cut at the crotch will do. If some limbs fall back in the way of the next cut, stop your saw and clear the area. If possible, cut so that you always keep the trunk between you and the guide bar (Fig. 4-6), and never limb higher than shoulder height.

The soundness of the tree wood should be determined. Look for rotten areas, weak roots, and weak sections in the trunk. Be aware of loose bark that may fall. Cat-faces (deformed tree trunk surfaces, usually caused by rot), old fire scars, and other abnormalities, especially at the base where the cuts are to be made, can greatly affect the amount of control you will have over the direction the tree will fall. Defects and abnormalities must be considered along with weight and direction of lean when judging the depth of cuts and holding wood needed. A small amount of rot may have little influence, but if the base of the tree is extremely rotten, the direction of fall may be limited and depend entirely on the

Fig. 4-6: Limbing a tree before it is felled.

Fig. 4-7: Plumbing the lean of a tree.

lean of the tree. Remember also that frozen wood is more brittle, and additional holding wood may be needed in the winter.

Check the tree for loose bark and remove any that will interfere with the felling process. Loose bark, higher up the tree, can be dislodged with a long pole if it can be reached. Use the axe to remove loose bark and check for soundness. Internal or hidden rot can often be determined by thumping on the tree with the axe after the bark is removed. Caution needs to be taken at this same time because you may dislodge loose bark or broken limbs from above. This is fast becoming a lost art, but with a little experience you will be able to judge the amount of rot from the hollowness of the sound.

Possibly the most important step in the pre-felling process is to correctly determine the lean. None of the subsequent felling steps will function properly if the lean is misread. Sometimes a tree has an obvious lean that is easily read, while another can be much more difficult because of slope or its relationship with other standing trees. Generally, most trees lean down the hill, but occasionally you will find an exception to this. Therefore, never take anything for granted.

To plumb a tree for lean, you can use an axe or a weight, such as a saw wrench, attached to a piece of string. Stand back far enough so your plumb line will cover a good portion of the tree. Hold the axe or wrench (Fig. 4-7) so it will swing freely, head down. Sight along the plumb line from the center of the stump up toward the tree's top. Do not sight along the side of the tree, as the taper will make it difficult to judge the lean. Take one reading and then move around the tree 90 degrees and take another. This will determine the heaviest lean and also if there is a side lean to contend with. The weight of the lean can be judged from the amount of the tree that is over the center line, and this can be helpful later on when deciding the depth of cuts and amount of holding wood needed.

After you have determined the direction in which you want to fall the tree, plan for your escape routes. Always have one primary escape route, and in case the tree goes the wrong way, have a secondary escape route. If you have to drop the tree at an angle uphill, make your escape route at least a 90-degree angle away from the intended direction of fall, being careful not to go below the felled tree or directly behind the butt. As soon as you know that the tree is coming down, use your escape route to get as far away from the butt of the tree as possible before it hits the ground. While making your retreat, turn your saw off and put it down. Holding onto the saw will only slow you down if you have to escape. Removing this heavy object from your hands greatly increases your agility and should be done every time you fell a tree.

It is not safe to fell a tree straight up a steep slope. The tree may bounce as it hits the ground and jump back over the stump or to either side. It is impossible to foresee what the fallen tree might do and consequently for you to select a safe place to watch its fall. It is also not wise to fell a tree straight down a steep slope, since it is apt to be shattered by the fall—particularly if the terrain is rough. In addition, it is bad practice to fell a tree across a large rock, a log, or a stump. Obstructions like these tend to break the trunk and cause much waste of good timber. Felling across a gulley or over a sharp ridge may also shatter the trunk or at best make subsequent limbing and bucking operations difficult.

Before felling any tree, study it as if you were descending the tree to observe its limbs or those of adjacent tree tops that may have been broken out and could possibly snap back toward you. A large tree trunk can be used as protection if it is a safe distance from the butt of the felled tree. Often times, the trunk of a falling tree will whip sideways upon impact. In the case of a tree felled uphill, loose rocks or logs may be dislodged and may come down next to the butt. Never make your escape route 180 degrees away from the direction of fall. If the tree should kick back, because of unusually large limbs on the tree or as a result of striking some object on the ground, it will probably travel directly over the stump. This escape route has proven more dangerous to fallers than any other cause. Again, make your escape routes at nearly right angles to the intended direction of fall and in such a manner as to clear yourself from possible whiplash of the trunk or rolling debris.

If there is any appreciable wind, do not cut at all. With large trees, check the top, as the wind may not be noticeable at ground level but have a great deal of effect higher up. A light, steady wind may be used to an advantage, but if it is gusty, unpredictable, and begins to have a great deal of influence on the direction of fall, work should be suspended.

It is always safer to work with a crew of two or three, so that at least one person—and preferably two—can act as lookout. At first glance, the job of lookout seems like a simple task. This is not the case. It can quite often be a tedious task, especially with just two men—a faller and a lookout. The three-man system is the most effective and safest. Let us look at both methods, beginning with the two-man system.

While there are several systems by which the lookout can warn the faller of danger, the most effective system places the lookout 4 or 5 feet (120 or 150 cm) away from the faller with a stick approximately 3 feet long (90 cm) in his hand. The lookout watches the tree, and if he sees danger, he strikes the saw operator on the shoulder. This system removes the lookout from the immediate work area, but leaves no chance for error in warning the operator. That is, if danger should develop and the lookout strikes the saw operator, the operator should immediately exit the area. Leave the saw right where it is, as it would only impede the operator's exit. The saw operator should look at the lookout and follow him to safety. Do not take off irrationally and end up running right into danger. Again, look at the lookout and follow him to safety.

In the three-man lookout system, the man who will warn the saw operator will stand in the same position as with the two-man operation. Rather than watch the tree, he will watch the third man, who will position himself so that he can easily watch the falling operation, yet can be seen at all times by the faller and second lookout. In order to prevent fatigue, the best position for the lookout is either flat on his back or sitting down. Both faller and lookouts should agree on a signal system whereby the faller and the lookout can be headed for safety at the first sign of danger. A wave of the hand or similar motion should do. The lookout should also point in the direction in which safety is assured. The lookout positioned next to the faller can signal the faller by striking him on the shoulder and at the same time head in the direction pointed to by the first lookout. The faller will follow him, leaving the saw behind.

Not until all the sizeup and prework are completed can the tree be felled. Again, you must be properly attired before the actual saw work can be started. In extremely dry, dusty conditions, a breathing mask insures more operator comfort.

Felling the Tree

The first step in the actual felling of a tree is to make an undercut (Fig. 4-8). This undercut is made in the side of the tree facing the direction of fall. Before starting, however, make sure you have enough fuel to completely fell the tree before you make any cuts in it.

Positioning the undercut is the most important factor in determining where the tree will fall. (Many beginners mark the undercut notch and back cut with chalk to serve as a guide.) Place your first cut on the side of the tree in the direction of fall. This cut should be perpendicular to the planned direction of fall. The cut should be one-third of the total diameter of the tree if you are cutting a sound tree. A heavy lean or butt rot in the tree may make it necessary to reduce the depth of this cut.

Fig. 4-8: Steps in felling a tree.

To complete the undercut, start your second cut above the first cut at an angle, so that these two cuts will meet at the back of the first cut. As a minimum, the opening of the undercut should be one-third of the undercut's depth, or 1 inch (2.5 cm) vertical for every 3 inches (7.5 cm) horizontal. This is a minimum, and the opening should be slightly larger than this. The easiest way to make this cut is to hold the saw on the side of the tree at the back corner of the bottom cut. The bar of the saw will be slightly higher than the engine. As you make your cut, apply downward pressure on the bar. Continue this downward pressure without moving the engine until you see the wedge settle down. At this point, remove the saw from the cut and then remove the undercut. The second cut should be high enough so that the notch will have an angle between 35 and 45 degrees (Fig. 4-9A). If the wedge of wood will not come out freely, knock it out with an axe. Never walk in front of a tree that has been undercut.

Figures 4-9B and C show two variations of the so-called standard undercut. In recent years, many professional fellers have found that with the chain saw, they can just about as easily make the undercut upside down with the sloping

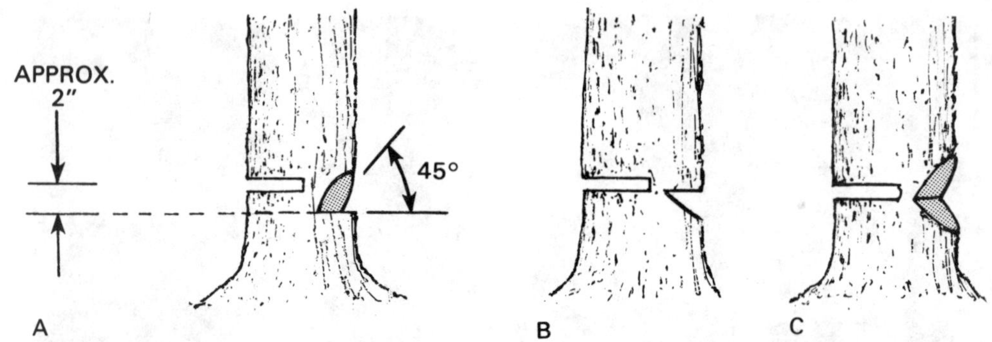

Fig. 4-9: The standard or traditional undercut (A) is commonly used for small trees. The undercut shown in B leaves a butt end of log cut squarely across the log, while C illustrates a popular variation of A that is often used on sloped terrain.

Fig. 4-10: Improper undercuts such as these can cause plenty of problems.

side coming up from below (Fig. 4-9B). This Humboldt undercut, as it is called, makes a more nearly square end on the butt log and saves lumber that is lost with the traditional undercut. However, regardless of the type of undercut used, it must be complete and clean to direct the fall of the tree. If made improperly, the undercut can cause problems (Fig. 4-10); if made correctly, it will effectively relieve the support of the tree on this side and allow an empty space for the tree to close. This will effect a smooth pivot when it falls. The notch will prevent a barber-chair (Fig. 4-11), causing the butt to kick back. This is now the time to determine if the heartwood is sound or rotten. Do not put more than one undercut in a tree.

A barber-chair is usually caused by unusually strong pressure within the tree, causing it to split up the trunk. The backside of the tree snaps violently and quickly out and up. Usually, some point of the tree, a short distance up the trunk from the cut, acts as a pivot for this action, similar to a teeter-totter. The tree will usually remain balanced at the point during at least part of the descent, but will fall off to one side of the butt or the other just before or at the time it makes contact with the ground. Occasionally during descent, the tree will use this point as a slide and will come back over the stump a considerable distance before falling off. This all happens extremely fast, and unfortunately the faller may be in the way. Trees with an unusually large amount of lean are prone to do this also. Use extreme caution when cutting these. Cleanly removing the undercut will help to eliminate this hazard. Treat every tree as if the worst could happen. Because of the possibility of a barber-chair, most of your cutting should be done standing

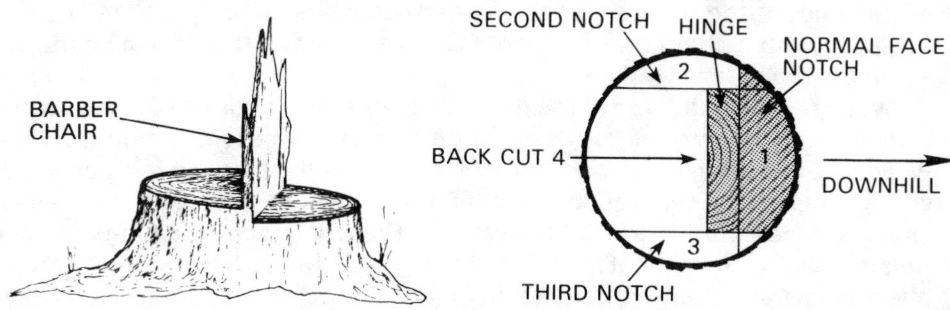

Fig. 4-11: Most barber-chair stumps (left) are caused by a tree having a heavy downhill lean. With a proper sequence of cuts (right), a barber-chair stump can be prevented.

at the side of the tree, not behind it. Again, directly behind the tree is the most dangerous spot during the felling operation.

Before starting the final or back cut, always recheck the area for people, animals, or machinery. Double check your undercut and direction of fall. Have good footing, a firm grip on the saw, and start your back cut. The back cut should be level and approximately 2 to 4 inches (5 to 10 cm) above the horizontal cut of the notch or undercut. Cut from the side of the tree where there is least danger, but preferably on the side of your primary escape route. After the cut is started, swing the saw around and cut a short distance into the two sides of the tree. This is called "cornering" and it prevents the bark and the sides from tearing when the tree falls.

As soon as your cut is deep enough, pound a plastic wedge (Fig. 4-12) into the middle of the cut. This wedge will prevent the tree from settling on your guide bar. The wedge should be tapped further in as you progress with the cut. The engine should be stopped each time the wedge is driven in, and the wedge should not contact the chain or guide bar. Use a long plastic wedge which will not damage your saw.If the tree is frozen, use only light taps to prevent the wedge from

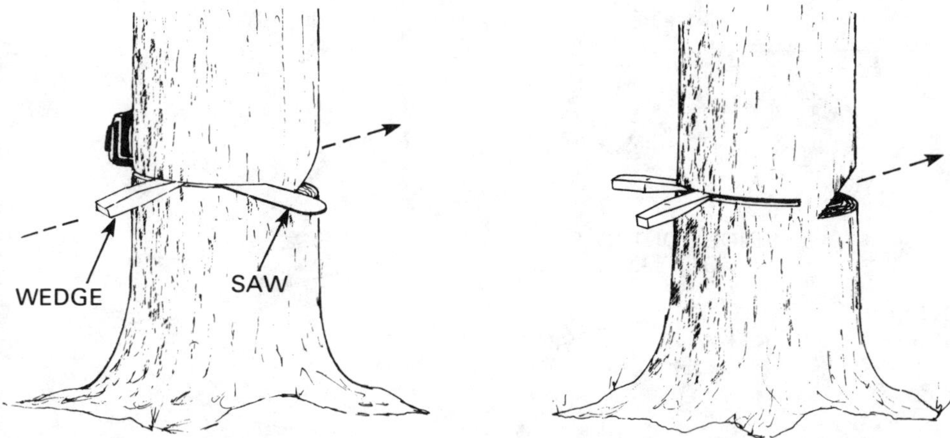

Fig. 4-12: Proper placement of wedges.

popping out or the top from snapping and coming down on you. If your saw is equipped with a chain brake, it can be activated rather than stopping the saw when driving plastic wedges.

If you are felling the tree in the direction of its lean, continue your cut perpendicular to the direction of fall, being careful not to leave a large amount of "hold wood," or uncut wood, on one side or the other. If the tree is a fairly good size, check to make sure that your bar is cutting all the way through. Never, under any circumstances, cut the tree all the way off. Hold wood acts as a hinge and controls the direction of fall (Fig. 4-13). If you cut all the way through, this hinge effect is lost and the tree may fall in any direction.

A barber-chair stump can frequently be prevented by making special cuts, as shown in Fig. 4-11. That is, once the notch has been cut, make a small notch on each side. After these small notches are cut—they should reach no farther in than the sapwood—the back cut is made in the normal manner.

To complete the felling operation, continue the back cut, watching for any movement that may indicate the tree is ready to fall as before. Never cut the back cut all the way to the notch. Uncut wood must remain to act as a hinge to control the fall of the tree. The hinge thickness should be about one-tenth of the tree diameter, or on an average-size tree, the hinge should be about 2 inches (5 cm) thick. If there is no hinge, the tree will set down on the saw and could fall in any direction. As the back cut begins to widen and the tree starts to fall, shut the saw off, remove it from the cut, set it on the ground, and retreat along your predeter-

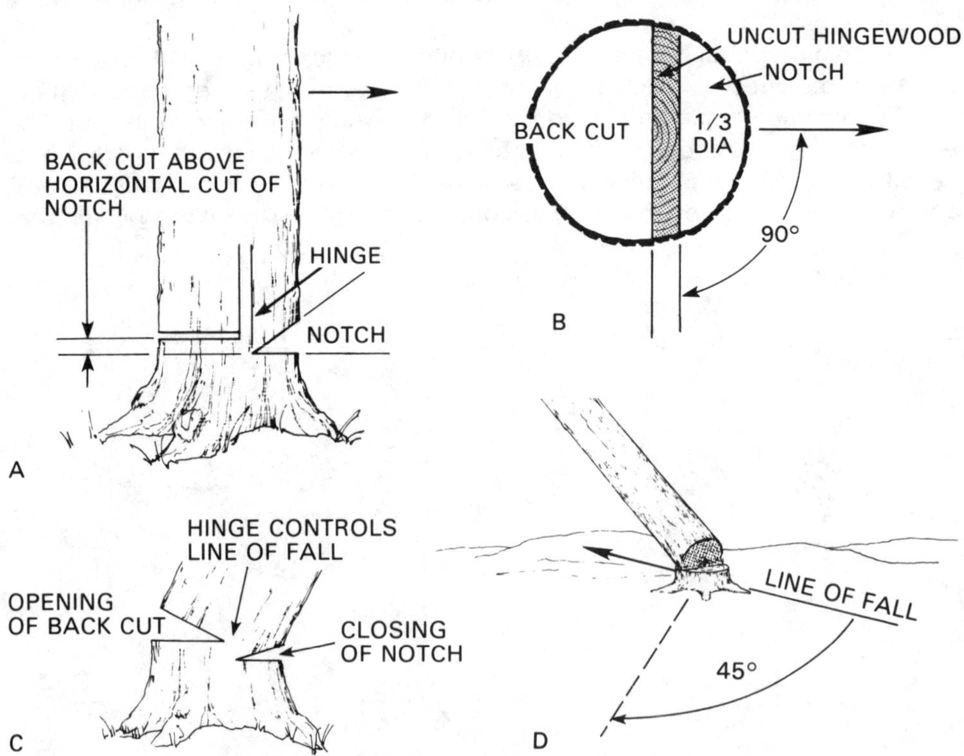

Fig. 4-13: How the back cut is made. Never cut through the hinge.

mined escape route. Always keep your eyes on the tree so that you know what it is doing at all times. Many fallers have been injured because they have neglected to do so.

There are two instances when you should call out a warning to others that may have entered the felling area. One is before you start the saw to begin the back cut. Call out, "Round the hill," if the tree is to be sidehilled, "Down the hill," if the direction of fall is down the hill, or "Up the hill," if the tree is going to fall up the hill. The other time to call a warning is just before the tree begins to fall. Shut off the saw and call out one of the above warnings, but only if you can safely do so.

After the tree is down, do not return to the area immediately. Allow a few minutes for widowmakers (loose branches) to come down, and always beware of limbs and tree tops kicking back from whiplash of the falling tree.

Special Problems of Trees

There are special problems almost every time you decide to fell trees. Fortunately, most of them are easy to solve by using specific techniques such as described here.

Correcting Lean. To fell a leaning tree away from its natural line of fall, a technique known as "cornering" can be used to alter the tree's course to some degree. First, make the undercut, as you would under normal conditions, in the direction you want the tree to fall. But, to increase the directional power, the end of the hinge closest to the desired line of fall is left thicker than the other end (Fig. 4-14). That is, start your back cut on the side where you wish to leave the narrow hinge, working it in the direction of the wide hinge. Stop when there is about two to three times the amount of wood in the wide hinge as there is in the narrow hinge. Generally, the tree will begin its fall when you reach this point, or you can start it on its way by using wedges. The wedges should be driven into the back cut in line with the desired direction of fall and should be kept as tight as possible until the tree begins to go.

When felling a tree away from its natural line of fall under confined conditions—around one's home, near power lines, and other similar obstructions—a

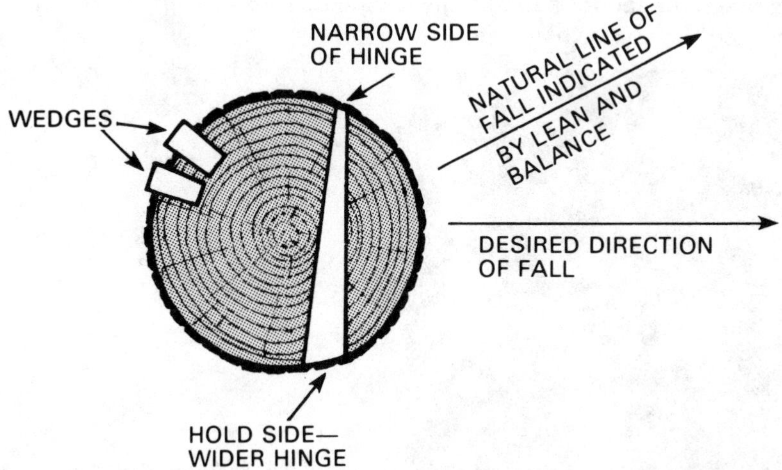

Fig. 4-14: To fell a tree away from its natural line of fall, it must be "cornered" as shown.

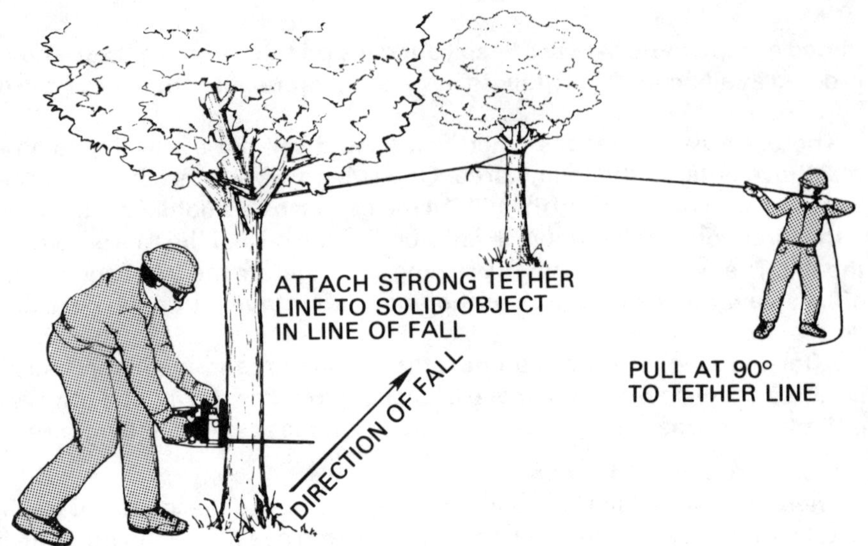

Fig. 4-15: A block-and-tackle and pulley arrangement is the best way to fell a tree under confined conditions. The higher up that the rope is fastened, the better the leverage that is obtained.

single pulley or a block-and-tackle setup is usually needed to control the direction of fall (Fig. 4-15). This is a two-man job: the faller and the rope handler. The latter person must locate himself *at least* twice the tree height away, since the tree will be falling in his direction.

Since tree height is very easy to misjudge, it is important to know, when working in a confined area, how far the tree will reach when it falls. One of the easiest ways of accomplishing this is to place a ladder or pole of known height at the base of the tree. Then, walking back to what you approximate to be two tree lengths, hold a small stick at arm's length (Fig. 4-16), aligning the top of the stick with the top of the ladder and the end of your thumb with the bottom of the ladder. Then, visually move the ladder's length up the tree. The number of increments times the ladder's length gives you the tree's height. Perform this several times to confirm your estimate.

Fig. 4-16: Method of determining the height of a tree.

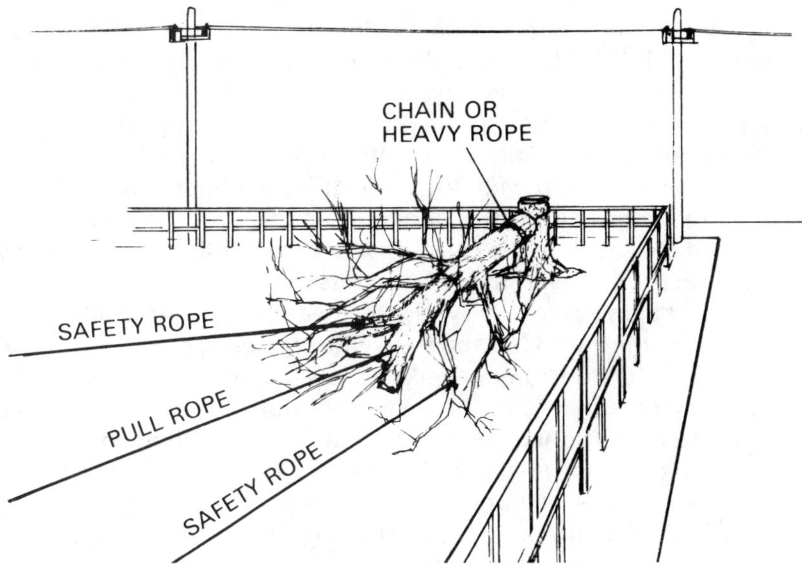

Fig. 4-17: Method of guiding a medium sized tree to the ground.

Medium-sized trees can frequently be handled as shown in Fig. 4-17. The heavy safety ropes can be fastened to other trees or to heavy vehicles. The pull line or chain should be operated by a rope handler. Only heavy rope in good condition should be used in any tree felling operation.

In some confined space situations, it is far better and safer to have the tree felled or topped by a professional tree contractor. Then, you can limb it and buck it into firewood-size logs. In this way, you will usually save money and have the wood, without endangering yourself or damaging property.

Rotten Trees. Rotten butted trees present special problems. Before cutting a tree, as stated earlier in the chapter, the trunk should be sounded for rot with the heel of an axe or hatchet. If a hollow or mushy sound is heard, you will have to be more alert than usual, since rotted wood has little holding power. Quite frequently, it is possible to make the felling cuts high enough to avoid the worst of the rot. This not only results in safer felling, but also saves the time required to saw rotten wood off the butt. When the rot goes up too high for this, it may be

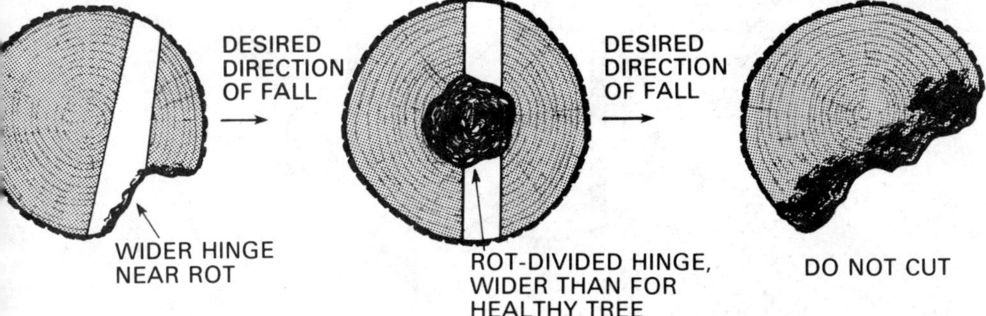

Fig. 4-18: Different locations of rot and how it should be cut.

possible to saw around the rot by employing the cornering technique used for leaning trees (Fig. 4-18). Otherwise, the felling cuts should be planned as though the rotted wood were already cut away.

Cutting Larger Trees. When a tree is too large to be cut with a single pass of the saw, a special technique must be employed. For example, if the tree to be cut has a diameter larger than the length of the guide bar but not twice its size, use the following technique: After the undercut has been made, hook the bottom bumper spike of the saw into the tree about 3 inches (7.6 cm) behind the back of the notch, so that the saw will stop before it hits the hinge wood. Using the bumper spike as a pivot point, carefully swing the guide bar into the trunk until the bar is perpendicular to the line of fall and even with your pivot point (Fig. 4-19A). You may have to reposition the bumper spikes a few inches to complete the first cut. But, be careful not to cut into the hinge or hold wood. The saw is then removed from the cut and repositioned directly behind the tree. When knocking out the center portion of the wood (Fig. 4-19B), be very careful of kickback. Continue to pivot the saw around the tree until the hinge is reached and the tree begins its fall (Fig. 4-19C). Frequently, wedges are required to hold the back cut open and to tilt the tree towards the undercut.

If the diameter of the trunk is more than twice the length of the guide bar, first make the directional undercut (Fig. 4-20A). Then, bore (see Chapter 3) straight into the tree from the undercut, as shown in Fig. 4-20B. Never plunge the nose of the guide bar straight into the wood. Instead, speed up the engine and press the bar nose against the angular notch, using it as a guide. Then, slowly pivot the engine while continuing to press the bar nose until it is into the wood double the bar width. Be very careful of kickback when making this boring cut. When completed, remove the saw and move to the other side of the tree to make the next cut. Make the second cut by pivoting the guide bar into the cut (Fig. 4-20C), leaving a properly sized hinge. Remove the saw from the cut and reverse its position for the third cut (Fig. 4-20D). Continue to saw around the trunk making fan-like cuts (Fig. 4-20E); insert a wedge when the half-way point is reached.

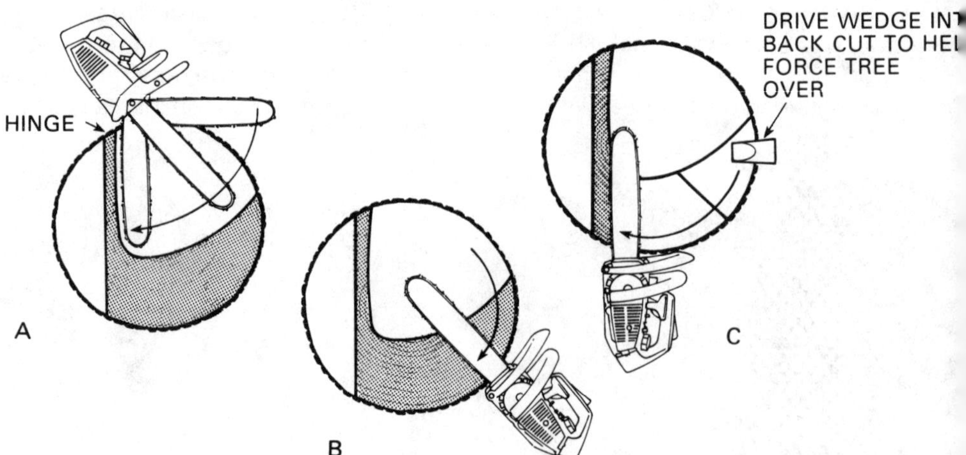

Fig. 4-19: Steps in felling a large tree whose diameter is larger than the length of the guide bar, but not twice its size.

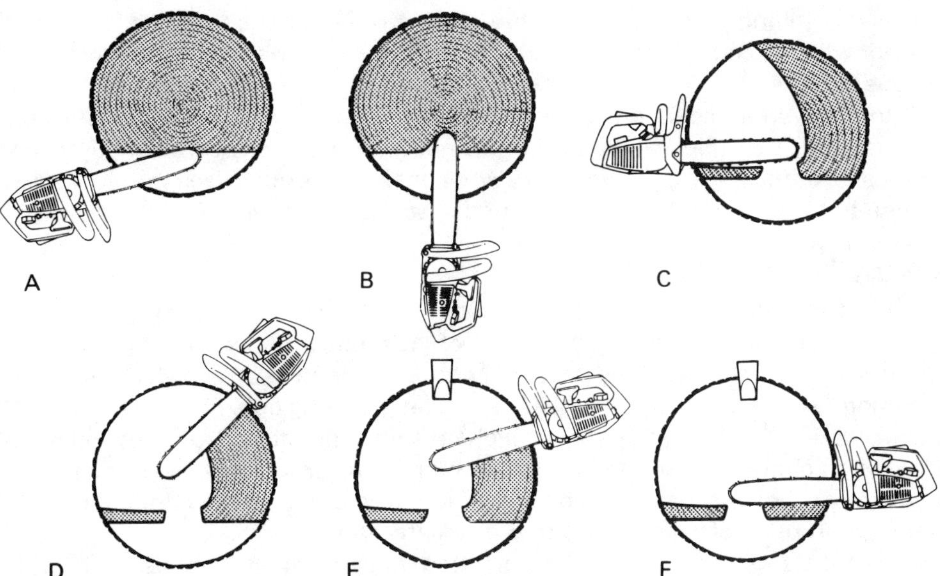

Fig. 4-20: Steps in felling a large tree whose diameter is more than twice the length of the guide bar.

The final cut is made by drawing the saw forward in the cut to reach the hinge (Fig. 4-20F). If the tree does not fall at this point, drive in additional wedges.

Freeing A Hung Tree. Even the best fellers sometimes lodge a cut tree in a standing one. A sturdy limb on either the tree being felled or the tree in its way may fail to bend as expected, or the cut tree may fall or twist a little out of line. Since dislodging may be difficult, it is important to seek professional help and equipment.

Freeing A Stuck Saw. If a saw gets bound when making a back cut, chances are that this could have been prevented by the proper use of wedges. In fact, the easiest way to free a stuck saw is to start a wedge and drive it in far enough to release the saw. If this fails, borrow another saw or use an axe, and make the

Fig. 4-21: Freeing a stuck saw with a wedge.

necessary felling cuts well above the stuck saw. After the tree has fallen, the weight will be taken off of the trunk and the saw kerf can then be opened with a wedge.

If the saw should become stuck while bucking, the use of a wedge in the kerf will usually free it (Fig. 4-21). If this does not work, make a cut with another saw or an axe just beyond the bound saw. When making the cut to free the stuck saw, remember the rules of cutting logs under stress given earlier in the chapter.

PRUNING CUTS

It is often necessary—both in the woods and at home—to make pruning cuts. Of course, the pruning of a tree consists of the removal of dead, dying, diseased, interfering, objectionable, obstructing, and weak branches, as well as selective thinning to lessen wind resistance. For making pruning cuts of more than 2 or 3 inches (5.1 or 7.6 cm) in diameter, a chain saw is practical. But, never climb a tree when operating the saw. In fact, as mentioned previously, never make any cuts above shoulder height. Jobs higher in a tree or where a falling limb could damage property should be left to a tree care professional.

When making a pruning cut, keep in mind that cuts must be made sufficiently close to the trunk or the parent limb, without cutting into the branch collar or leaving a protruding stub. To prevent splitting a limb or peeling the bark from the trunk, the three step method shown in Fig. 4-22 is recommended. The first cut is an undercut that should be made a few inches away from the trunk. The second—a top cut—will remove the limb, leaving a stub. The third cut removes the stub, leaving a smooth surface that will become part of the trunk. It is important not to cut into the trunk or shoulder wood. Nutrients that feed the tree are carried throughout its length just under the bark.

Treatment of cuts with wound dressing is optional except where open wounds in certain trees may attract insects that carry disease or allow fungus invasion. If such treatment is made, materials nontoxic to the cambium layer must be used, and care must be taken to treat only the exposed wood with a thin coat of dressing. On trees known to be diseased, the chain saw should be disinfected with methyl alcohol at 70 percent (denatured wood alcohol diluted appropriately with water) or Chlorox solution after each cut and between trees where there is known to be a danger of transmitting the disease on the saw.

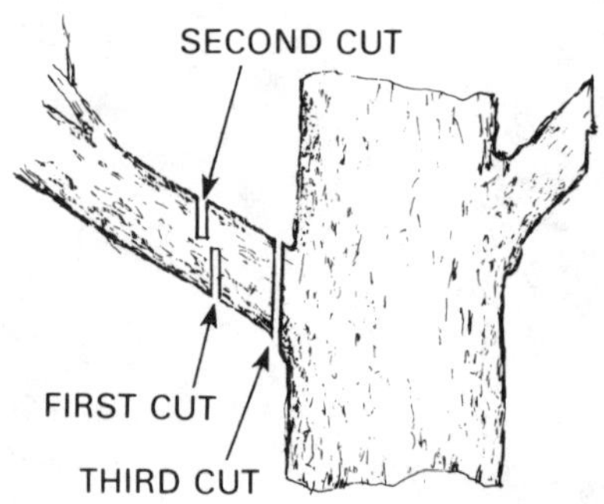

Fig. 4-22: The three step method of pruning a limb.

5 Your Chain Saw and Firewood

The popularity of fireplaces and woodburning stoves has skyrocketed in the past few years. In fact, wood fuel now accounts for all or part of the space heating requirements in over five percent of all American households. Besides the pure pleasure a warm, crackling wood fire can provide, the rising costs and spot shortages of other heating fuels, such as oil, coal, and natural gas, have caused this resurgence of wood as a fuel source. Yet heating with wood will not automatically lower your fuel bills, especially if you buy wood from a dealer who, quite understandably, is out to make a profit. Real savings can be made, however, if you find, cut, and season the wood yourself. That is when your chain saw can turn into a big money saver. As detailed in the previous chapters, supplying yourself with wood is a lot easier than most people think and the rewards are great.

Some fuels are pollution and health hazards, but wood is much lower in irritating pollutants than most fuels. Most individuals generally consider wood smoke with nostalgia. Wood smoke permeating the air makes our visit to historical villages seem all the more authentic.

Wood has a low ash content. It burns cleanly, leaving only a minimum of waste as ash. The ash that remains can be useful for gardening; applied to the soil it is a valuable fertilizer. In using wood, you are utilizing a renewable fuel resource. Coal, oil, and gas are limited resources. Once used, they cannot be replaced. But new trees can be grown, so that after a few years, more wood is available. Wood has the advantage of being readily available, easily cut, and relatively inexpensive. Fossil fuels, by contrast, require expensive equipment, plus considerable manpower and energy, to locate, extract, and process.

The wood that you use in your fireplace or stove might very well be unusable in any other way. By burning it in your fireplace, you can help reduce the burdensome piles of wood waste riddling our environment in woodlands, urban dumps, and around wood industries. Reclaiming it for firewood provides a worthwhile environmental alternative.

Selecting Good Wood

Before going out and obtaining wood for your fireplace or woodstove, draw up some general guidelines concerning your needs and desires. All wood possesses certain characteristics which can vary greatly from one type of wood to the next. While heating value is usually the main concern when choosing what wood to burn, there are many other things to consider. They include: (1) ease of splitting; (2) ease of starting; (3) extent of sparking; (4) extent of smoking; (5) quality of coals, or the ability to form long-lived coals; and (6) amount of aroma.

The heat that is derived from the combustion of wood depends upon the concentration of: (1) woody material; (2) resin; (3) ash; and (4) water. The first three features vary depending on the tree species and its growth rate, while the latter depends on the species, the season in which the tree was cut, and the seasoning procedures used. In general, the heaviest woods, when seasoned, have the greatest heating value. Lighter woods give about the same heat value per pound as heavier hardwoods, but, because they are less dense, they give less heat per cord or cubic foot. For example, black locust wood has almost twice the density and weight as the same volume of white pine, and it has twice as much heat energy. Of course, excessive moisture in firewood reduces its fuel value. Wood containing 20 percent moisture content—which is considered the normal for air dried condition—will lose about 3.5 percent of the net heat content of dry wood as a result of moisture evaporation losses. In contrast, wood containing 50 percent moisture will lose about 8.6 percent of the net heat due to the presence of moisture. The heating values per air-dried standard cord of numerous varieties of wood as compared to other fuels are given here:

A Cord of Air-Dry Wood equals		Tons of Coal	Gallons of Fuel Oil	Therms of Natural Gas	Kilowatt Hours of Electricity
Hickory, Hornbeam (ironwood), Black locust, White Oak, Apple	=	0.9	146	174	3800
Beech, Yard Maple, Red Oak, Yellow birch, Ash	=	0.8	133	160	3500
White and Gray Birch, Walnut, Cherry, Soft Maple, Larch, Ponderosa Pine	=	0.7	114	136	3000
American Elm, Ash, Red Cedar, Yellow Pine	=	0.6	103	123	2700
Poplar, Cottonwood, Willow, Aspen, Hemlock, Spruce	=	0.5	86	102	2200
Basswood, White Pine, Balsam Fir, White Cedar	=	0.4	73	87	1900

Assumptions...

Wood: 1 cord = 128 cubic feet of wood and air or 80 cubic feet of solid wood at 20% moisture content. Net or low heating value of one pound of dry wood is 7,950 Btu. Efficiency of the burning unit is 50%.

Coal: Heating value is 12,500 Btu per pound. Efficiency of the burning units is 60%.

Fuel Oil: Heating value is 138,000 Btu per gallon burned at an efficiency of 65%.

Natural Gas: One therm = 100,000 Btu = 100 cu. ft. Efficiency of burning is 75%.

Electricity: One KWH = 3,412 Btu. Efficiency is 100%.

Fuelwoods are grouped into the following three main classifications: hardwoods, softwoods, and fruitwoods, each with their own set of advantages.

Hardwoods. For a long lasting fire, one of the heavier hardwoods, such as oak, ash, maple, hickory, or birch, provides an excellent fuel source. These species burn less vigorously and with a shorter flame than most softwoods. Hardwoods generally produce a steady, glowing bed of coals. Excessive amounts of smoke and sparks are uncommon.

Softwoods. Softwoods, such as pines, spruces, and firs, are rapid burners and ignite easier than most hardwoods. These woods make exceptional kindling; however, fires built entirely of softwoods burn out quickly and leave no bed of coals, so frequent attention and replenishment must be given to them. The resins present in these woods can also cause some problems. These resins collect in chimneys and stovepipes as combustible creosote deposits which can increase the chances of dangerous chimney fires. Frequent cleaning of chimneys or stovepipes is necessary when these woods are the only source of fuel. Sparks and smoke may be more plentiful than in hardwood types. Actually, some resinous softwoods, such as cedar, juniper, larch, hemlock, and spruce contain moisture pockets which can be troublesome. Upon heating, trapped gases and water vapor build up pressure in these pockets, resulting in "pops" which throw sparks. Such sparking can be a potential fire hazard especially in fireplaces without proper screens. Sparking is another reason to reduce the moisture content of wood as much as possible before burning. Of course, most softwood aromas are excellent, and the softwoods are good if you want a quick warming fire or a short fire that will burn out before you go to bed or step out for the evening.

Fruitwoods. Fruitwoods often combine the best characteristics of both the hard- and softwood types but are usually the most difficult to find in large quantities. Apple, cherry, citrus, and other fruitwoods burn with steady heat-producing flames and pleasant aromas. Smoke and sparks are uncommon, but starting fruitwood fires can sometimes pose a problem.

Anything more than wide generalizations are impossible to make when discussing the three basic wood types. Splitting, burning, and heating characteristics can vary greatly among woods of the same class. For instance, the splitting characteristics of wood—very important if you cut your own firewood—are affected by the number of knots in the logs and by its lengths. Short lengths of straight-grained, knot-free wood will split easily. Green wood and softwoods usually, but not always, split more easily than dry wood and hardwoods. As a general rule, frozen wood splits very easily.

The table on pages 68 and 69 gives detailed information on some of the more popular firewoods. The figures given are approximations, but they can be used in drawing comparisons between specific woods.

Of course, certain fuelwoods are native to particular areas of the country, and if you plan to locate and cut your own firewood, your selection may be even more limited. Yet every geographical area in the United States offers a good variety in available woods. With a little patience and work, the home woodcutter can fulfill his or her needs with a suitable timber.

When and Where To Get Wood

Nine-tenths of the people in developing nations around the world depend on firewood as their chief fuel source. The search for wood in many of these coun-

Species	Type of Wood	Heat Value (Hickory = 100)	Density (Water = 1)	Btu/Cord (Millions)	Air Dried Pounds Per Cord
Alder	Hard	49-53	.38-.40	15.6	2100
Apple	Fruit	83-84	.58-.62	27.2	3900
Ash	Hard	81-82	.57-.61	22.1	3100
Aspen	Hard	53	.37-.39	14.7	2100
Basswood	Hard	53	.35-.37	14.1	2100
Beech	Hard	89-91	.64-.66	24.5	3700
Birch, Black	Hard	82-86	.62-.69	24.8	3800
Birch, White	Hard	76-79	.57-.61	20.9	2900
Birch, Yellow	Hard	80-82	.59-.63	23.6	3400
Butternut	Hard	70-71	.49-.53	14.5	2900
Cedar, Red	Soft	71-76	.45-.47	17.8	2800
Cedar, White	Soft	52-54	.31-.35	11.7	2100
Cherry	Fruit	70-71	.50-.52	19.0	2800
Citrus	Fruit	93-94	.66-.69	25.4	3600
Cottonwood	Hard	52-54	.33-.36	15.3	2100
Cypress	Soft	48-55	.43-.47	11.1	2300
Dogwood	Hard	100-107	.70-.79	27.4	3900
Elm, American	Hard	71-80	.50-.59	21.3	3000
Eucalyptus	Hard	61-64	.44-.49	17.2	2400
Fir, Balsam	Soft	51-54	.36-.40	14.1	2000
Fir, Douglas	Soft	64-69	.45-.51	15.4	2500
Hemlock	Soft	57	.40-.42	15.3	2100
Hickory	Hard	100	.70-.74	27.2	3900
Ironwood	Hard	104-106	.76-.81	30.1	4300
Juniper	Soft	61-64	.45-.50	15.2	2700
Locust, Black	Hard	95-98	.69-.70	27	3900
Magnolia	Hard	74-76	.47-.51	21.2	2900
Maple, Hard	Hard	83-88	.58-.65	26.4	3700
Maple, Soft	Hard	67-73	.47-.54	19.2	3200
Oak, Black	Hard	86-94	.60-.66	24.5	3600
Oak, Red	Hard	86-94	.60-.66	24.1	3600
Oak, White	Hard	95-100	.68-.73	26.4	3900
Osage, Orange	Hard	112	.78-.83	27.2	4100
Peach	Fruit	88-92	.61-.68	25.9	3800
Pear	Fruit	86-91	.63-.67	25.2	3700
Pecan	Hard	87-93	.62-.66	26.1	3800
Pine, Ponderosa	Soft	59-61	.40-.42	15.3	2500
Pine, Sugar	Soft	51-53	.36-.38	13.8	1900
Pine, White	Soft	50	.35-.37	14.4	1900
Pine, Yellow	Soft	68-71	.38-.61	19.4	2800
Plum	Fruit	82-85	.67-.72	27.2	3800
Poplar	Hard	57	.40-.42	15.4	2100
Redwood	Soft	47-54	.33-.40	13.5	2200
Sassafras	Hard	62-63	.44-.46	17.5	2900
Spruce	Soft	59	.41-.44	15.6	2100
Sycamore	Hard	70	.49-.52	18.7	2700
Walnut	Hard	74	.52-.55	21.1	3200
Willow	Hard	53	.36-.38	14.7	2000

Ease of Splitting	Ease of Starting	Extent of Sparking	Extent of Heavy Smoking	Quality of Coals	Amount of Aroma
Good	Fair	Little	Little	Fair	Slight
Poor	Poor	Little	Little	Good	Excellent
Good	Fair	Little	Little	Good	Slight
Good	Good	Little	Moderate	Fair	Slight
Good	Poor	Little	Moderate	Poor	Slight
Poor	Poor	Little	Little	Good	Slight
Good	Good	Moderate	Little	Good	Slight
Good	Good	Moderate	Little	Good	Slight
Poor	Good	Moderate	Little	Good	Slight
Good	Fair	Moderate	Little	Good	Good
Good	Excellent	Moderate	Moderate	Poor	Good
Good	Excellent	Great	Moderate	Poor	Good
Good	Poor	Little	Little	Excellent	Excellent
Poor	Good	Little	Little	Good	Excellent
Good	Fair	Little	Moderate	Fair	Slight
Good	Fair	Little	Moderate	Fair	Fair
Poor	Good	Little	Little	Good	Fair
Poor	Fair	Little	Moderate	Excellent	Slight
Poor	Poor	Great	Moderate	Fair	Heavy
Good	Good	Moderate	Moderate	Poor	Slight
Good	Good	Little	Great	Fair	Slight
Poor	Good	Little	Moderate	Poor	Good
Poor	Fair	Moderate	Little	Excellent	Slight
Poor	Poor	Little	Little	Excellent	Slight
Poor	Good	Moderate	Moderate	Good	Good
Poor	Poor	Little	Little	Excellent	Slight
Good	Fair	Little	Little	Good	Good
Poor	Fair	Little	Little	Excellent	Good
Good	Fair	Little	Little	Good	Slight
Poor	Fair	Little	Little	Excellent	Fair
Poor	Fair	Little	Little	Excellent	Fair
Poor	Fair	Little	Little	Good	Fair
Poor	Poor	Little	Little	Excellent	Slight
Good	Fair	Little	Little	Fair	Excellent
Good	Fair	Little	Little	Fair	Excellent
Poor	Good	Little	Little	Good	Slight
Good	Excellent	Great	Moderate	Poor	Excellent
Good	Excellent	Great	Moderate	Poor	Excellent
Good	Excellent	Great	Moderate	Poor	Excellent
Good	Excellent	Great	Moderate	Fair	Excellent
Good	Fair	Little	Little	Excellent	Excellent
Good	Fair	Great	Moderate	Poor	Slight
Good	Fair	Little	Moderate	Poor	Slight
Poor	Poor	Little	Little	Fair	Excellent
Good	Excellent	Great	Moderate	Poor	Good
Poor	Fair	Little	Moderate	Poor	Slight
Good	Fair	Little	Little	Good	Good
Good	Good	Little	Little	Poor	Slight

tries has led to destructive deforestation and subsequent watershed damage. In America, the exact opposite is true. Under-utilization of our wood sources is more of a problem than shortages. Over 500 million acres (200 million hectares) in the United States are classified as commercial forestlands. When you consider that the average acre of woodland can yield between one-half to one cord of wood per year without damaging effects, the total volume of potential firewood in America becomes staggering.

Sensible, selective harvesting of timber from our woodlands will actually improve the quality of the remaining forest. You can get fuel from trees growing in the woods that are considered undesirable (Fig. 5-1). This includes trees that are poorly formed, diseased, of little-used or weed species—like pin cherry—and genetically inferior individuals. All such trees pose problems for the forest manager. They occupy valuable growing space which thrifty young trees might well use for continuing development. When diseased, these trees pose a hazard to nearby healthy trees. If genetically inferior, they may continue to reproduce and could keep the forest area full of poor-quality trees for generations to come. Weeding them out often costs more than can be returned for their commercial sale, but individuals interested in personal use find this practice worthwhile.

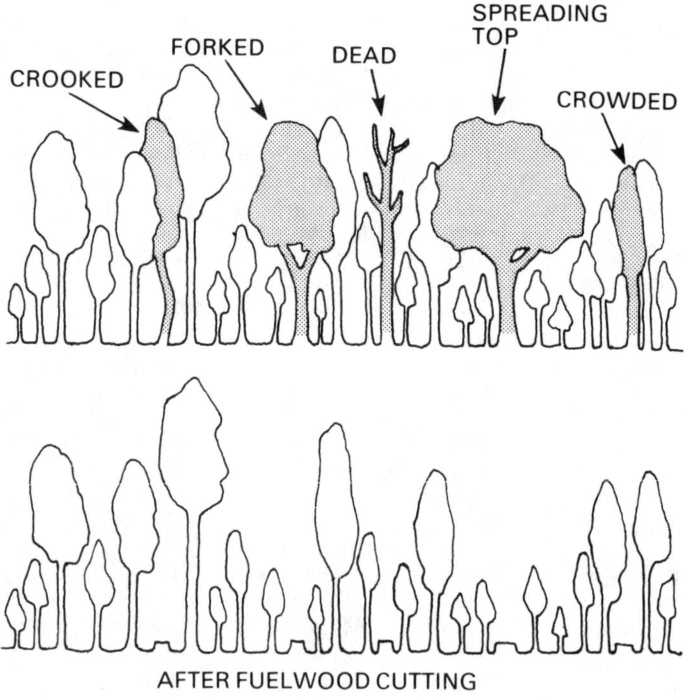

Fig. 5-1: A woodlot can be improved while gathering fuelwood.

For instance, a medium-sized tree with a 12- to 14-inch (30 to 35.6 cm) base is often considered too small for commercial harvesting. Yet such a tree will normally generate about one-half cord of wood, one quarter coming from the trunk and another from the branches. Trees of this size can easily be felled. Their logs are not too heavy to maneuver and are the ideal size for home splitting. Ten or 12 trees of this size can fulfill the winter firewood needs of the average household.

If you are fortunate enough to be the owner of a sizeable woodlot (20 acres or more), this type of responsible forest management can provide you with a perpetual source of fuelwood. But, to obtain the most economic value from your woodlot, cut those trees that will give more room for the growth of the best trees. Formerly, an owner frequently cut the straight, well-pruned trees for firewood, because they split easier than their crooked, limby neighbors. Such cutting rapidly reduces the timber value of the woodlot. Usually, the trees that should be cut are the poorest formed, the poorest pruned, and the lowest dollar value trees in the woods. Sometimes, of course, straight trees must be removed because they are crowding equally good or better trees. Try to space future timber trees an average of 20 feet (600 cm) apart.

If you do not own any wooded property and all the wood you own happens to be tied up in your furniture at the moment, do not despair. There are many other sources. For instance, many farms have wood available. As a matter of fact, roughly 40 percent of the wooded land in America is found on farms. Some farms are up to 60 percent timber, and often these stands need thinning out. It is most likely that you will have to contact several farm owners before finding one willing to allow cutting from his woodland; however, be persistent. Farms are just too good a firewood source to be passed over lightly. Some farmer may charge a slight stumpage fee, but this cost is often minimal.

Always be sure there is a mutual understanding between the land owner and yourself concerning exactly what is and what is not to be cut. Offer to put the agreement in writing if it will make one or both parties more comfortable. Respect the natural beauty of the land and always clean up any debris you may create. Starting off on the right foot with a cooperative farm or land owner can lead to years of trouble-free cutting.

Most National Parks and Forests (there are 164 National Forests in the United States) offer firewood collectors a chance to fill their woodsheds. In fact, the U.S. Forest Service has embarked upon an intensive nationwide program to make free firewood available for home use wherever it is available. The type of wood offered includes cull logs and slash resulting from commercial logging operations, windfall limbs and trees, smaller trees cut during thinning operations designed to improve the growth of timber left standing, and trees removed during the construction of roads and firebreaks. Regulations generally allow each family to cut and gather a specific amount of firewood (normally 10 cords) for home use at no charge. Woodcutting permits are required, however, and before one will be issued, the applicant must comply with prescribed regulations. Full information on obtaining permits to cut firewood on national public lands may be obtained from the local district ranger's office.

Many state parks and forestlands have also opened their doors to selective thinning by do-it-yourself woodcutters. Downed timber can be gathered easily, and in most cases, forest managers mark the standing trees they wish to have removed. State foresters, county extension agents, as well as county and city foresters can also provide you with information on local sources of firewood.

If you live in an urban area or other locality where standing woodland is at a minimum, look for firewood at nearby dumps or landfills. Since many local ordinances forbid open burning, the quantity of dead, discarded trees continues to mount on these lands which are sorely needed for the disposal of other solid wastes. As much as 30 percent of the debris in some town and city dumps consists of usable wood fibers, including the logs, limbs, and tops of trees toppled by storms. Removal of this wood saves the dump or landfill the cost of burying it, and this wood is generally free for the taking. But, be sure to seek official permission; some landfills and dumps sell salvage rights. The quality of dump or landfill wood is far from consistent; therefore, periodic checking to see what is available makes good sense. Utility company right-of-ways, land clearing operations, and areas that have recently been logged are other sources to be considered.

Firewood can also be obtained in the form of industrial wood scraps. Sawmills accumulate scrap materials such as slabs, trim, and edging in their millyards. Lumber companies often offer these materials for firewood at minimal cost, since this practice alleviates some of their hauling and burning problems. Logging operations also generate huge amounts of scrap timber suitable for cordwood (Fig. 5-2). Felled trees often accumulate on the sites of new housing or highway construction projects. In the past, these trees were often burned at the site, but new ordinances now require their being stacked and hauled away. Again, many operators would be happy to let you do this job for them.

Fig. 5-2: "Leftovers," such as these cull logs, are often made available by timber companies to firewood buying prospects.

Cutting and gathering firewood can be a year-round job. The cool autumn weather makes that time of the year the most enjoyable to work in, but do not plan on using any timber cut in the fall as firewood during the winter unless it is downed or dead and naturally well-seasoned. Felling trees in late spring and early summer has some advantages. Trees lose moisture through their leaves much faster than through their bark. So, if they are allowed to lay in place for a week or so before limbing, much of the moisture will escape through the leaves. Cutting in late spring and early summer also gives these trees the advantage of a few extra months of the hot sunshine necessary for proper seasoning. Whenever you decide to cut, remember that all fresh timber needs time to dry out before it is useful as fuelwood.

If you prefer not to gather wood yourself and plan to buy from a dealer, here are some buying tips to follow. Shop around and compare prices. Know exactly what

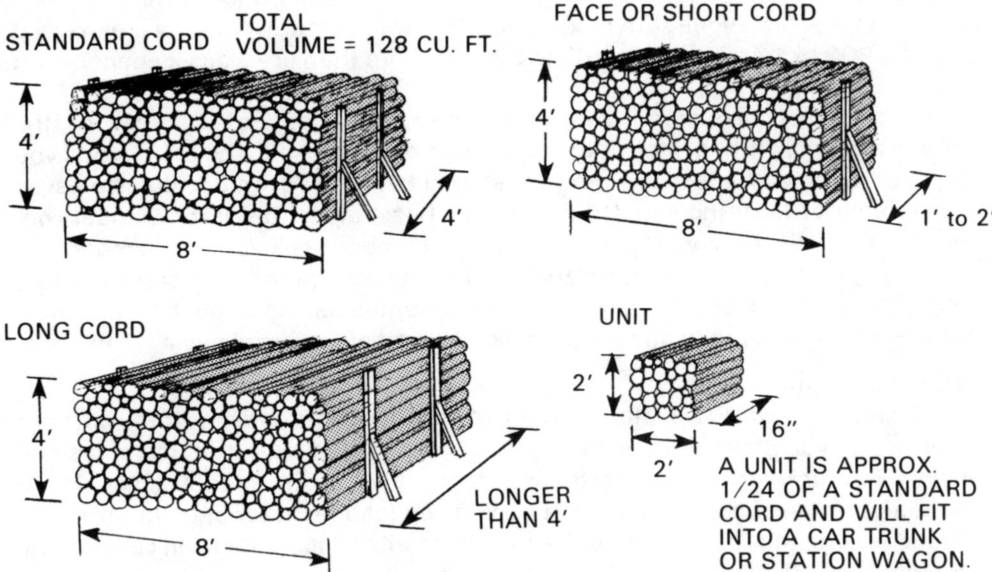

Fig. 5-3: Various firewood units of measurement. The law in many states requires firewood to be sold by the standard cord or a fraction of this unit only.

and how much you are buying. The most common measurement of firewood volume is a cord. A standard cord measures 4 feet by 4 feet by 8 feet (120 by 120 by 240 cm). But, all firewood measurement units (Fig. 5-3) include the air space between the sticks. Thus, the amount of solid wood depends upon whether the sticks are straight or crooked, round or split, and large or small in diameter. The variation is considerable as a standard cord may contain from 60 to 110 cubic feet (1.8 to 3.3 cu. m.) of solid wood. A commonly used conversion from gross volume to solid wood content of hardwood sticks 3 to 8 inches (7.6 to 20.3 cm) in diameter is 80 cubic feet (2.4 cu. m.) per standard cord. Larger diameters of round wood or split wood, neatly stacked, usually yield more solid wood per cord. Other factors to consider when buying wood are:

1. A standard cord cut into shorter lengths will always stack in less space than originally because many of the crooks are eliminated and some wood is lost as sawdust.
2. A standard cord contains about two to four times as much wood as a face cord, depending on stick length.
3. A cord of green wood will shrink at least 8 percent in volume during seasoning.

Firewood is sometimes sold by the load or by weight. Of course, the amount of wood in a "truck load" varies greatly depending upon the type of vehicle. A pick-up truck with a bed 4 feet (120 cm) wide, 19 inches (48.3 cm) deep, and 8 feet (240 cm) long will hold one 16-inch (40.6 cm) face cord. A dump truck may hold up to four standard cords. Large pulpwood trucks with a wood rack will hold from six to nine standard cords.

When buying wood by weight, try not to buy water; that is, **look for the driest wood possible.** In general, when dried to about 20 percent moisture content, dense hardwoods (oak, hickory, and maple) weigh about 4,000 pounds (1800 kg) per standard cord, while softwoods weigh half that amount. A cord of green wood weighs 800 to 1,400 pounds (360 to 630 kg) more than dry wood, depending on the species.

You can often save money by buying the wood in standard or longer lengths and recutting, splitting, stacking, and seasoning it yourself. The more wood you buy at one time, the less expensive it should be. Off-season buying also saves you money. Late spring and summer are the best times to buy. From January on, prices rise, and the supply of well-seasoned wood drops. But, remember that gathering fuelwood and cutting and splitting it to the proper size can be a most enjoyable pastime for the entire family. For a number of people such healthy outdoor exercise as sawing and splitting wood is part of the fun of having a fireplace.

Transportation

When you buy from a dealer, you can arrange for home delivery. If you cut your own wood, you probably have to haul it yourself. Traveling a hundred miles and back for a truckload of wood certainly will not save you any money. If you do not own a vehicle capable of hauling a good-sized load in one trip, team up with a friend or two and rent a truck or heavy-duty trailer. Lightly-sprung cars pulling regular duty trailers work fine for hauling small loads short distances on good roads, but even when dry, a cord of wood can weigh as much as two tons, and the rough roads of a forest can easily damage all but the toughest equipment.

One of the major problems when bringing logs out of the woods is finding a convenient stacking or loading point. It is usually no problem to cut access trails suitable for a heavy-duty truck or jeep by felling small trees or pruning back overhanging limbs, but any number of obstructions may make it impossible to pull fallen logs directly to these access trails or a storage point.

While a four-wheel drive jeep or truck equipped with a front-mounted winch is ideal for solving this problem, the use of a snatch block or a block-and-tackle and several lengths of 1/2 inch (1.3 cm) or thicker rope can serve the same purpose. Simply attach the pulley to a convenient tree and pull the line in a direction which will move the log around the obstruction (Fig. 5-4). When there is open passage to the access trail and the pulling vehicle must move along at an angle to this route, a snatch block positioned at the side of the trail solves the problem.

Once you have maneuvered the logs out onto the access trail, a logging sled or skid pan is the best way to transport the logs to the stacking or loading site. Construction of a simple skidding sled is no major task. Cut out the wooden runners on a band saw, and use sturdy pieces of 4 inch by 4 inch lumber (10.2 by 10.2 cm) for the cross beams. Raise the cross beams well off the runners so they will clear small obstructions. The pulling rope or chain can be attached to the heavy ring bolt fastened in the center of the front cross beam (Fig. 5-5). Use a peavey to roll the logs up a ramp of short poles and onto the sled. Fasten them securely with rope or chain, keeping as much of the log off the ground as possible. This reduces friction and dirt accumulation.

Skid pans, flat steel pans with rounded-up front ends, serve the same purpose as skidding sleds. The pans should be chained as close as possible to the pulling vehicle. This raises the pan's front end, again reducing friction and drag. Remember, you can easily strain all but the strongest vehicles if you try to move too much at one time.

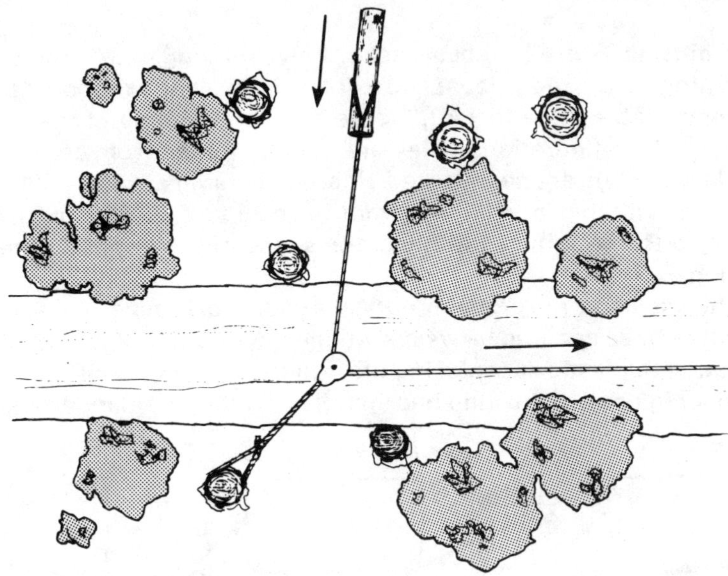

Fig. 5-4: Method of using a pulley or snatch block to skid a log in confined areas.

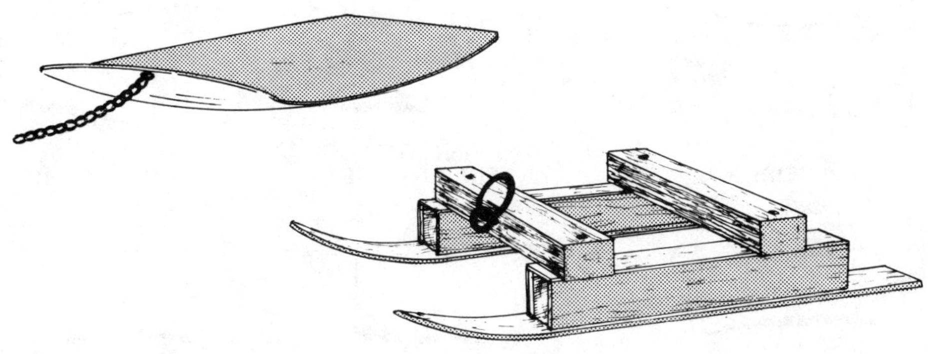

Fig. 5-5: Typical log skid pan for small logs.

SPLITTING WOOD

Whether you gather your own wood or buy it from a dealer in standard cord sizes or larger, some splitting is usually necessary for the wood to season more quickly. In other words, the whole idea behind splitting is to reduce the wood's moisture content. Some tree barks tend to retain moisture more than others. Because of this, some large logs take an *extremely* long time to release their moisture unless they are split. Wood splitting can be done by hand or by using a power splitter.

Splitting Wood By Hand

When done the right way and with the proper tools, splitting wood by hand can be both fun and healthy exercise. Done improperly, it can be a backbreaking, dangerous task.

Hand Splitting Tools. The basic set of hand splitting tools should include an axe, a splitting maul, and at least two iron wedges. Your axe should be both personally comfortable and efficient. Figure 5-6 shows some of the more widely used axe head configurations. They are usually forged from carbon tool steel, and the blades or bits are heat-treated. Head weights vary from 1-1/4 to 5 pounds (.6 to 2.25 kg), with hickory handles from 14 to 36 inches (35.6 to 91.4 cm) long. In addition to the weight of the head, the shape of the handle is important for comfort (Fig. 5-7).

Since the axe head will probably outlast a couple of handles, be sure to choose an axe with a head secured by *visible* wedges. Avoid axes with handles molded to the head with plastic as replacing the handle will be very difficult. Also avoid varnished or glossy, paint-finished handles which are dangerously slippery

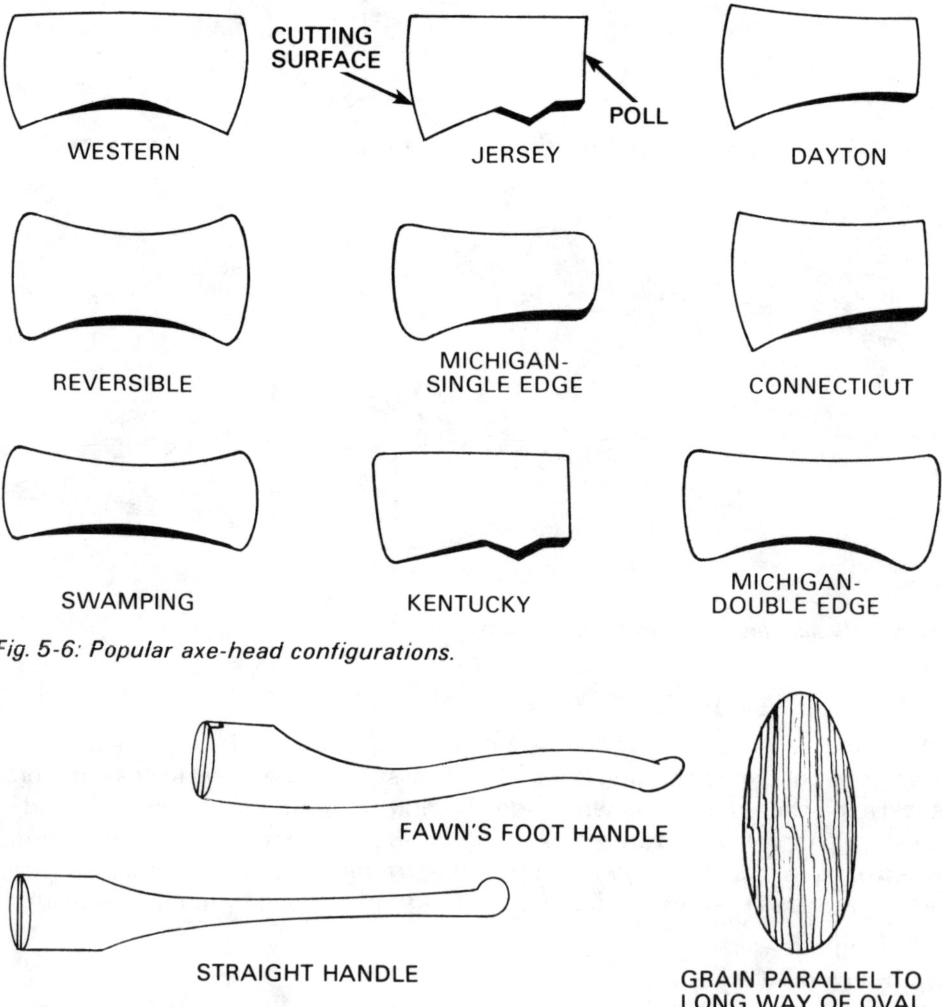

Fig. 5-6: Popular axe-head configurations.

Fig. 5-7: Two popular handle shapes. The grain of the handle should be parallel to the way of the oval (right).

when wet and will cause blisters. The handle should be of good, straight-grained hardwood; hickory is the best. The grain should run parallel to the length of the handle to prevent warping and breakage.

The double-bit axe is usually used to fell, limb, or prune trees and to split and cut wood. It is also used for notching and shaping logs and timbers. The single-bit axe may be used for the same purposes; in addition, the poll is used to drive wedges.

Extremely cold temperatures can make even the finest steel heads brittle, so warm your axe blade up before use on winter days. Leaving axes lying about on the ground is quite dangerous. When not in use, secure your axe with the blade sunk into your chopping block or some other log. Never hang an axe by its head.

The woodchopper's maul (often called a splitting axe) is designed especially for splitting wood (Fig. 5-8A). It is also used in conjunction with wood-splitting wedges (Fig. 5-8B), first for making a notch with the splitting edge, and then to drive the wedge with the striking face opposite the splitting edge. Mauls are forged from high-carbon steel, are heat-treated, and usually are made in 6- and 10-pound (2.7 and 4.5 kg) head weights with approximately 32-inch (81.3 cm) hardwood handles.

A

B

Fig. 5-8: (A) Using a woodchopper's maul for splitting a log; (B) Using a maul with a wedge to split a log.

The correct maul strike is an accurate one, not a forceful one. Mauls can power their way through even the most stubborn logs without much help from you. Misplaced maul swings are often very unforgiving on the tool's handle. The great head weight and swing momentum make split or shattered maul handles more of a possibility than with axes. So be extra cautious and precise when swinging a maul.

The wood-splitting wedge is forged from a solid piece of high-carbon steel and may be heat-treated. Wedges are made in various patterns, the ones illustrated in Fig. 5-9 being the most commonly used. Weights range from 3 to 8 pounds (1.4 to 3.6 kg). Square-head, Oregon splitting, and stave wedges are designed

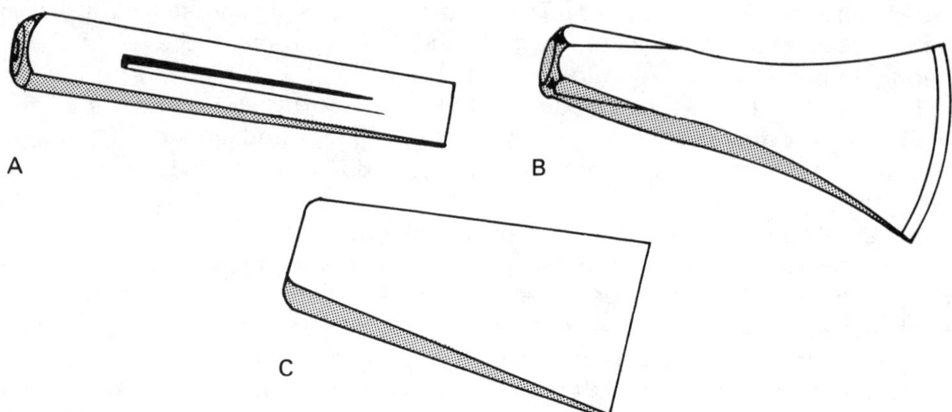

Fig. 5-9: Three major types of wedges: (A) square head; (B) Oregon; and (C) stave.

for splitting logs, firewood, staves, and other wood products. Always use a woodchopper's maul or an axe to make a starting notch. A wedge should be struck with a sledge or woodchopper's maul having a striking face that is larger than the head of the wedge. Do not use plastic or aluminum wedges described earlier in the book when chain sawing, because they will not survive the rigors of wood splitting.

Care of Hand Splitting Tools. For efficiency and safety, an axe must be kept sharp. The bluntly tapered edge of a new axe is great for splitting but too blunt for limbing. Two axes, each sharpened differently, are ideal; but a single axe can be sharpened to a medium taper and serve effectively for both uses.

After the original edge has been formed, periodic resharpening will be required. Place the head in a vice and run an angled file from the heel to the toe over the entire length of the blade. Turn the axe frequently and concentrate on forming an even edge over the entire blade. After the nicks have been removed, use a circular stone to hone with a circular motion at about a 25-degree angle. First use the medium side and then the fine side of the stone. An Arkansas or moon stone will perfect and polish the edge. Always use plenty of sharpening oil when using a stone, as it keeps the stone's surface from clogging with steel particles.

Eventually, the handle of an unused axe will dry out and the head will be dangerously loose. Soaking the axe head overnight in a bucket of water usually solves this problem. Sometimes additional wedging will be necessary. Storing an axe with the head resting on a dirt floor will keep the wood fibers in the handle swollen and the head tight.

To replace an axe handle, rest the heel of the handle on the floor and gently tap the head onto the handle. Next, with the head resting on the floor, strike the handle heel sharply with a mallet until the handle is tight. Take off the shavings that have been forced from the handle with a wood rasp. Drive in hardwood wedges (Fig. 5-10A) along the sides as far as they can go and trim them. Finally, drive in two iron wedges (Fig. 5-10B) alongside the wooden wedges.

Both mauls and wedges should also be kept sharp and free from nicks in their cutting edges. Maul handles should be given the same care as axes.

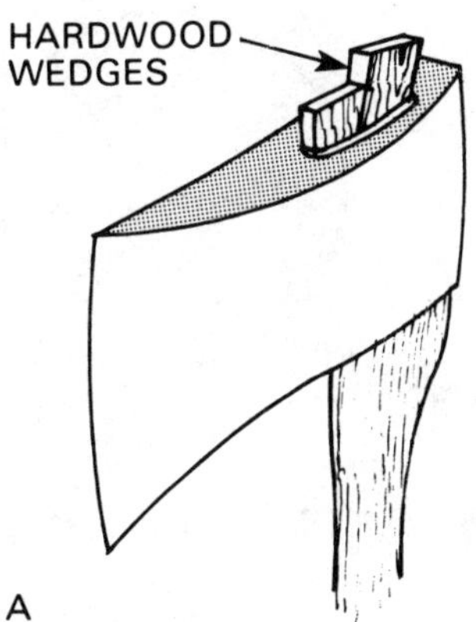

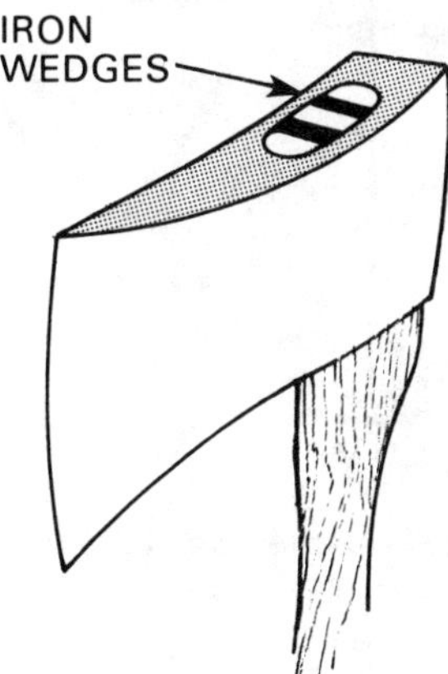

Fig. 5-10: Steps in installing a new axe handle.

Hand Splitting Operation. It takes practice to learn to split wood safely and efficiently. Learning to read the flow of the grain and working with this flow rather than against it will make your wood splitting task much more enjoyable. Grain patterns differ between tree species and a straight-grained ash will always split easier than an elm with its interlocking and interweaving wood fibers. The grain also varies within a tree and will prove to be most difficult around branches and knobs.

Never split wood directly on the ground as this is a good way to strike a rock or your foot. Place the piece to be split on a chopping block which can be either a larger log or a stump about 20 inches (50.8 cm) high. Draw an imaginary line across the piece to be split in line with any natural crack or with the center. Drive in your axe or maul along that line as many times as it takes to form a split. Flex your knees when you swing so that the angle between the log and your axe is 90 degrees. If it does not split, drive a wedge in at the center; two wedges placed halfway between the center and the edge may be needed with large or stubborn blocks. Wedges carefully placed can also be used to free a buried axe or maul.

Most medium- or large-sized logs are split in half. This is accomplished by placing the wedge in a medullary ray or crack beyond the center of the log (Fig. 5-11A). If the first wedge does not split the log, or if it no longer drives easily, a second wedge should be started along a near-side medullary ray, so that the split will bisect the log. Some large logs of interlocking fiber woods may require three or more wedges to split.

Another popular method of splitting large logs is called "daisying." This method, as shown in Fig. 5-11B, is fast and does not require driving wedges. You simply work around the outside, splitting off the sections like daisy petals. Follow the basic marked cuts, but it is usually not necessary to move the log or walk around the chopping block.

Still another method of splitting large logs is to cut them in pie-shaped pieces (Fig. 5-11C). With all splitting techniques, remember that the main purpose of doing the job is to expose as much wood as possible to air and to make the wood small enough to handle easily. Of course, the size of the pieces will depend on where they are to be used: fireplace, furnace, or stove.

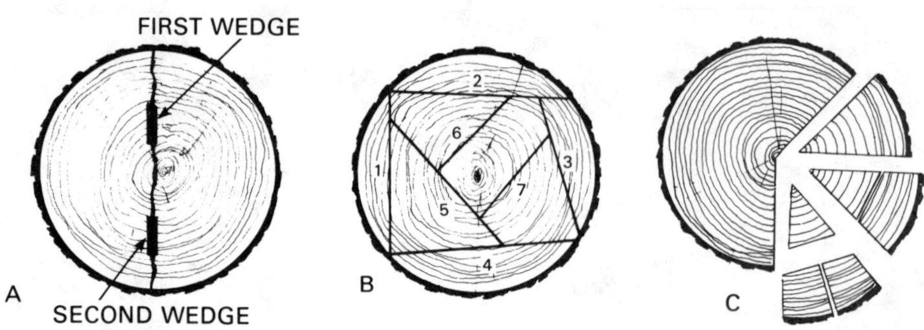

Fig. 5-11: Three methods of splitting large logs: (A) Halving; (B) daisying; and (C) cutting them into pie-shaped pieces.

As shown in Fig. 5-12, a crotched log is the best way to steady an uneven piece on the chopping block. If logs have branch stubs or knots in them, the split line should run through the center of the knots or stubs. Curves in the grain of the bark often indicate knots which have been overgrown and hidden. Looking for humps in the bark is another good way of spotting hidden knots. Some splitting experts advocate placing the piece to be cut on the block tree-top end up. Others prefer placing it base-end up. Use whatever way works best for you, but study and learn the natural grain of the wood and always cut with it.

Fig. 5-12: A crotched log will help steady an uneven log for splitting.

While a crotched log may be helpful in supporting wobbly pieces on the block, splitting such a log can prove to be a problem. There are two ways to handle a crotched log. You can saw the legs apart (Fig. 5-13A) and split them individually (Fig. 5-13B), or stand the piece on its legs and drive a wedge in on line with the legs' centers (Fig. 5-13C).

Green or semi-dry wood usually splits better than dry, well-seasoned wood, and softwoods, in general, split easier than most hardwoods or fruitwoods. As mentioned earlier, frozen wood often splits quite easily, although it may be more difficult to pound wedges into it. This wedge problem can usually be solved by cutting a starting notch into the log face with your chain saw. No matter what wood you choose to burn in your fireplace or stove, you will find that a straight grain and an absence of knots will make nearly any wood splitting job an enjoyable task.

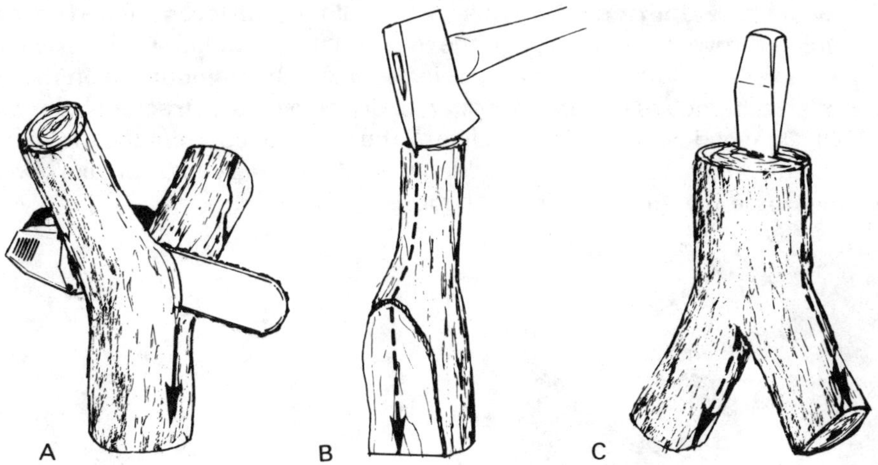

Fig. 5-13: Two methods of splitting a crotched log.

Power Splitters

Power splitters do take a great deal of the work out of splitting. They do the work much faster, too. Therefore, if you plan to do a large amount of cutting—and splitting—wood, it may be wise for you to consider the purchase of a power splitter. With a splitter, the work involved in splitting a log includes the lifting and setting of the log on the splitter, moving away, and starting the splitting process. During the operation of the splitter, keep hands and arms away from the machine. There are two types of power splitters: the hydraulic-wedge type and the screw or cone type.

Hydraulic Splitter. With this type of splitter, the log to be split is rested on a metal beam or pan, and a hydraulic cylinder then pushes the log into a steel wedge to split the wood. Designed to handle 24-inch (61 cm) or longer logs, they can be coupled to the hydraulic system of a farm tractor or can be driven by their own power source (Fig. 5-14). Heavy-duty models generate 10-ton (9 metric ton) splitting forces.

Fig. 5-14: Types of hydraulic splitters: (left) Gas and (right) electric-powered.

Screw or Cone Splitters. With this type of splitter, the log is pushed up to the cone, which screws its way through the log until the log splits. These units (Fig. 5-15) are available with their own power source, can be mounted on the rear wheel of an automobile or garden tractor, or driven by a farm tractor power take-off (PTO). On wood with interlocking fibers, the screw or cone splitters frequently have difficulty in splitting the wood cleanly. And, in some cases, an axe or maul may have to be used to complete the job.

Fig. 5-15: A screw-type log splitter.

STACKING, SEASONING, AND STORAGE OF FIREWOOD

After the firewood has been cut and split, it must be carefully stacked and stored to permit the wood to season properly. This work, as well as that of final bucking or cutting the logs to desired length, is done on your home grounds. This final bucking can be done on a sawbuck, such as described in Chapter 3, or in a cutting crib, such as the ones shown in Fig. 5-16. Cutting cribs make it possible to cut many logs at the same time. The logs can be piled together, and one pass of the chain saw will cut them all to precisely the same length.

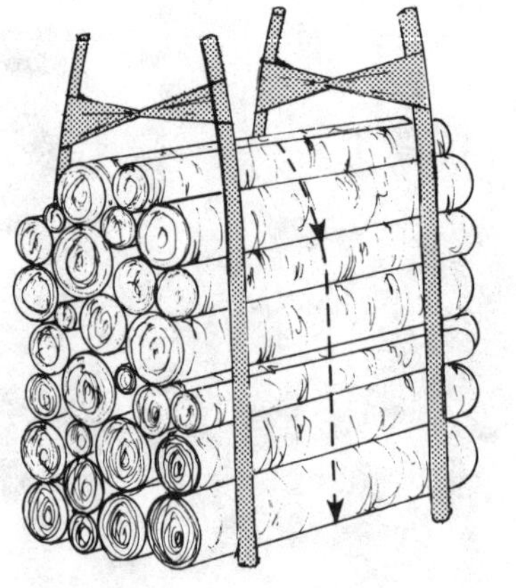

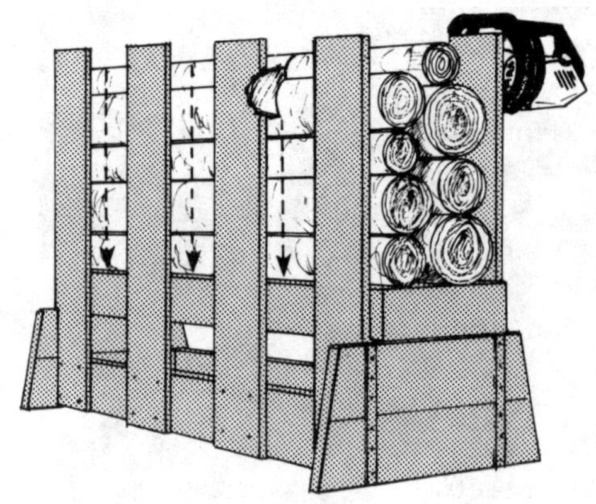

Fig. 5-16: Typical cutting cribs.

Fig. 5-17: While electric log splitters are most popular for backyard use, they can be used in conjunction with a generator for splitting in the woods.

Most log splitting done by the do-it-yourself woodcutter is also done on home grounds. This is the reason for the great popularity of hydraulic electric log splitters (Fig. 5-17). Most, if not all, seasoning and storage of firewood is done at home.

Seasoning Firewood

Green wood will burn, but seasoned or dry wood is lighter, has more heat value, and is less apt to form creosote deposits. Any moisture in the wood reduces the recoverable heat because water absorbs heat in the process of being changed to steam. The net heat from a pound of completely dry (no moisture) hardwood is about 7,950 Btu. All wood has some moisture in it which reduces the net usable heat at a rate of 1,200 Btu per pound of water.

The moisture in the wood of living trees varies among species, within a species, and even within a single individual. Frequently, there is a significant difference between the quantity of moisture contained in the central column of heartwood of a tree and the outer layers of sapwood which is surrounded with bark. For example, freshly cut American beech has been found to have a heartwood moisture content of 72 percent. In contrast, heartwood moisture contents in American elm, northern red oak, and white ash are 95, 80, and 46 percent respectively. If you cut trees in summer, let them lie for a week. The leaves will draw moisture from the wood and dry it more quickly than if you limb the tree immediately.

Some woods, such as ash, beech, and Douglas fir, burn rather well after being only moderately seasoned, but to those who desire the maximum heating value available, proper seasoning and storage is a must. Seasoning time for green wood depends on a number of factors, but in most areas at least six, and preferably 12, months are necessary. With certain seasoning set-ups, such as solar driers, and in certain drier climates of the southwest and west, three months is often sufficient.

Temperature, air humidity, and exposure to rain and snow all affect drying time. When drying wood, the greater the surface area exposed to the air, the more rapid the drying. Therefore, stack the wood in loose piles that are raised off the ground. Wood greater than 8 inches (20.3 cm) in diameter or longer than 4 feet (120 cm) dries very slowly. Reduce the size of such sticks by splitting and/or sawing. Removing the bark from the logs will also help speed along seasoning, but this practice is too difficult and time-consuming to be practical. Elm wood accounts for one exception to this rule. Beetles often burrow beneath the bark of diseased elms and it should always be removed before any elm wood is brought indoors.

Firewood should be placed in an open area to obtain rapid drying and to prevent deterioration. The best wood drying piles are raised well off the ground, either supported by lengths of log, old lumber, or cinder blocks. Cinder or concrete blocks are ideal since they eliminate the loss of any logs to ground rot and last for years. Stack the logs loosely, allowing for maximum air circulation. The bottom layer should consist of halved logs placed slit side down on the support pieces. Stack the remaining halved, quartered, and smaller whole logs on top of this bed. Position these bark side up. (The curved water-resistant bark will act as a barrier against rain and help promote easy drainage of water through the woodpile.) Alternating each layer "log cabin" style (Fig. 5-18) will give support to the pile. Or, you can quickly construct a simple support system to hold your woodpile secure. End braces are a good solution to the problem of stacking wood. Constructed with 2 by 4's or logs, end braces are like book ends and can be built to accurately measure a standard cord. The boards or logs beneath the woodpile keep the bottom row off of wet ground. Your woodpile should always be located outdoors facing the prevailing winds and in direct sunshine whenever possible. Stacking the wood directly against the side of your house or other building retards both air circulation and sun exposure time. Insect problems can also arise in this situation, so an open area, well away from any living quarters, is the best spot to season your wood.

Gentle rains will not hurt the seasoning process, but covering the top of the stack with a sheet of clear plastic will guard against damage from soaking downpours. Thin 2-mil thick plastic is a bit too flimsy, but the 4-mil variety is sturdy enough to do the job and costs less than the 6-mil type. Secure the covering with

Fig. 5-18: Stacking wood log-cabin style or using end braces.

bricks or logs. On sunny days, the temperature within the covering will rise considerably, facilitating quicker moisture evaporation. Proper ventilation and air circulation is necessary so that the moisture escapes and does not condense on the plastic and drip back down into the woodpile. Since any clear polyethylene plastic sheeting will deteriorate when exposed to direct sunlight, you may have to replace your covering every few months.

Solar wood driers expand this heating principle to an even greater extent. Complete seasoning is often possible in as little as three to four months. If you need your wood within a relatively short time, or the climate in your area is not the best for easy drying, a solar drier may solve some of your problems.

Building a solar drier is not difficult. All it takes is some 4-mil polyethylene sheeting, a few pieces of sturdy framing lumber or logs, and a little time and common sense (Fig. 5-19). Again, the key is to keep the plastic sufficiently away from the wood to allow for proper air circulation. The high temperatures generated inside the dryer will hold insect problems to a minimum and keep the bark tight on the logs, resulting in a much cleaner fire. Heavy snow accumulations will rip the plastic, so a roof should be provided to keep the pile dry during the winter months.

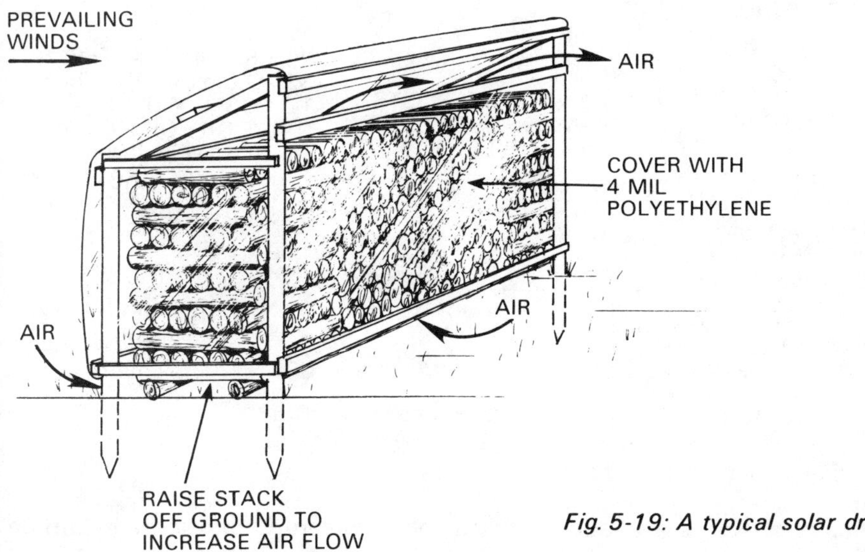

Fig. 5-19: A typical solar drier.

No matter which method you use, open air drying or solar heating, there are several ways that you can use to tell when your wood is properly seasoned and ready for burning or storage. Cracks appearing in the ends of the logs are a good sign of well-seasoned wood. When struck together, dry logs will sound with a sharp, crisp ring; green wood produces a dull, muffled thud. Checking to see if firewood is still seasoning can be done by simply weighing a few pieces on a bathroom scale. Record the weight and return the pieces to the woodpile, marking them for easy identification. Reweigh these pieces a few weeks later. If there has been a significant weight loss, drying is still taking place and the wood still needs more time to mature.

Storing Firewood

Once the wood has properly seasoned, you may wish to move it to a more convenient storage area. Outside, wood will dry to between 14 and 25 percent moisture content depending on humidity, temperature, and wind. In a garage or woodshed it may dry to 10 to 15 percent moisture content; and wood may dry to between 5 and 12 percent in the house. However, the best places to store firewood are outdoors, under cover, and near the house. Storing wood inside the home may be the most convenient, but this practice has several serious drawbacks—termite or beetle infestation, dirt and dust problems, and an added fire hazard. Wood kept in basements often absorbs moisture rather than losing it. A wood shed (Fig. 5-20), utility building, or free-standing garage is ideal. Firewood can also be stored in open areas, provided it is well covered with plastic or metal sheeting, or with a sturdy waterproof tarp. As in seasoning, proper air circulation, protection from ground rot, and protection from severe weather are the most important factors.

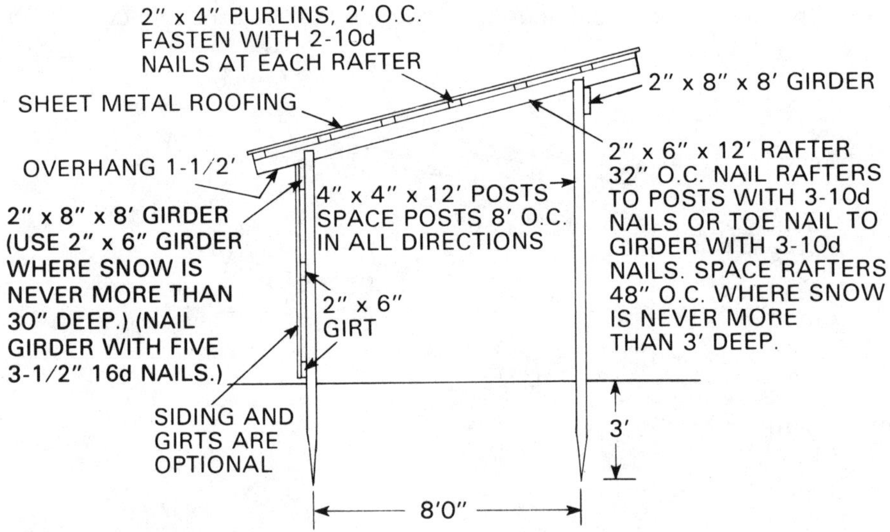

Fig. 5-20: Plan of simple wood shed.

If sufficient space is available under a roof, seasoning and storage can be accomplished in one handling. This practice eliminates the extra handling of moving wood dried outside into a covered storage area.

When bringing wood indoors, only take as much as you need for the day or evening. Metal containers such as old coal buckets or antique copper clothes boilers make decorative and practical indoor wood holders. They are just the right size for an evening's worth of firewood.

Construction of an inside wood box with loading access from the outside woodpile is especially convenient if you plan to burn large amounts of wood. Be sure the access door from the outside of the house is tight-fitting to prevent heat loss. Always plan your fuel storage for a minimum of handling, but remember that storing large amounts of wood inside the home can lead to more problems than it can solve.

Chain Saw Carpentry 6

The chain saw is a far more versatile tool than most owners tend to realize. Without being a skilled carpenter, you can use your chain saw to build patio, lawn, and rustic furniture; to construct sturdy, durable fences; to erect log cabins or other similar structures; and to create innumerable other useful items. In Chapters 7 and 8, there are various projects which you can build as is, or adapt to your individual requirements. But, before doing any specific projects, you should have some idea of basic chain saw carpentry.

BASIC CUTS IN CHAIN SAW CARPENTRY

General cutting, such as limbing and bucking, will quickly give you the feel of your chain saw and allow you an opportunity to practice the various basic cuts. Experiment on pieces of firewood or scrap logs until you become confident of your cutting techniques. Not everyone is a natural born carpenter, but with a little practice and perseverance almost anybody can build useful and beautiful things with their chain saw. A well-maintained and sharpened chain saw will help the carpenter tremendously. Successful carpentry begins with the straight line, and a well cared for saw will cut straighter, faster. Also, remember that when making any chain saw carpentry cuts, keep all of the safety rules given in Chapter 2 and other previous chapters in mind.

Crosscutting

Mastering the crosscut is the first step in learning the other basic cuts. It is the typical log sawing cut straight across the grain (Fig. 6-1). If you are to turn out satisfactory chain saw projects, you must know how to make a crosscut smoothly and at 90 degrees to the length of the log.

Fig. 6-1: The crosscut is the basic cut of all chain saw work.

Ripping

Cutting a log down its length with the grain is known as ripping. Rip cuts can be made with the log lying on the ground (Fig. 6-2A) or resting in a sawbuck (Fig. 6-2B). As shown in Chapter 7, ripping can also be done with the log standing on one end. But, regardless of the method used, be sure that the log is supported securely in place. When ripping vertically, keep your feet well back from the guide bar end projecting through the cut.

A

B

Fig. 6-2: Two methods of making a rip cut.

A chalk line on the log will serve as a guide. If a precision cut is required, place a plank parallel to the intended rip and use it to guide the bar in a straight line (Fig. 6-2A). When ripping, it often becomes necessary to drive wedges in the saw kerf to prevent binding. Also, when ripping softwoods, you must remember that there is a tendency for the saw to pull long, stringy fibers from the wood. These fibers must occasionally be removed from the area around the sprocket and the clutch drum, as well as the chain.

Boring

Boring or plunge cutting has been fully discussed in Chapters 3 and 4. In chain saw carpentry, you will need it to make corner joints, lap joints, and mortises (Fig. 6-3). To begin the cut, hold the body of the saw several inches lower than the nose of the bar. This counteracts the tendency of the moving chain to "crawl" up the log and also helps prevent kickbacks. Once a slot 1 or 2 inches (2.5 or 5.1 cm) deep has been formed in the surface of the log, pivot the saw's body up level with the slot, and press the nose of the bar straight into the log (Fig. 6-4).

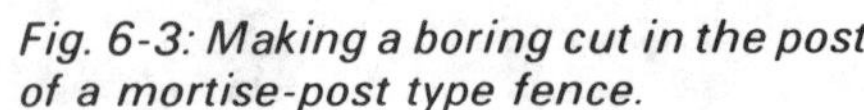

Fig. 6-3: Making a boring cut in the post of a mortise-post type fence.

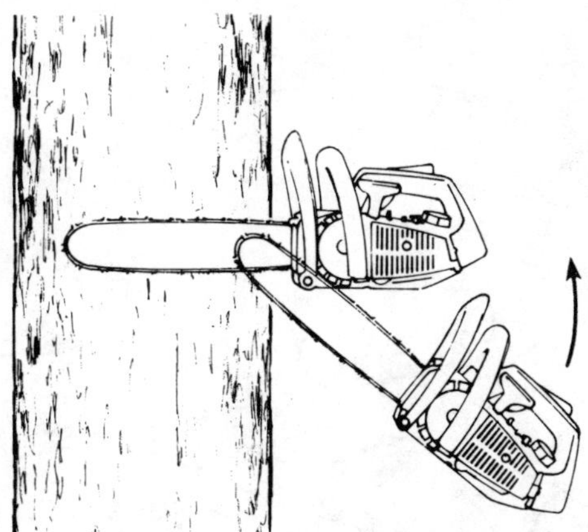

Fig. 6-4: When it becomes necessary to make a boring cut in log carpentry, be on constant guard against rotational kickback.

Hold the saw firmly, but do not force the chain into the cut. As always, the chain saw will do most of the work if you allow it. **Remember that boring is an extremely dangerous cut if care is not taken to guard against kickback.**

Corner Joints

Drawing a square onto the end of the log will help you visualize the 90-degree angle(s) your boring cuts must form when constructing a successful corner joint. Make a boring cut first, followed by two crosscuts to help define a notch of the required dimension. Repeat this step, making the second boring cut at a right angle to the first notch. You can continue around the log in this manner, making up to four square corners (Fig. 6-5).

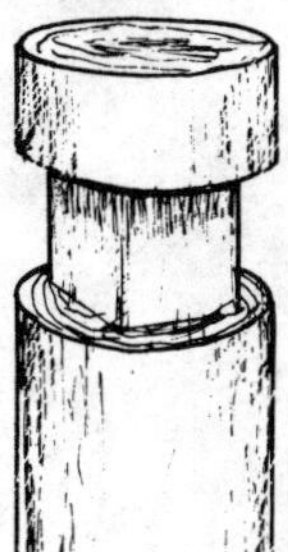

Fig. 6-5: Steps in making a corner joint.

Lap Joints

The three basic types of lap joints are illustrated in Fig. 6-6. Each joint is named according to its portion on the timber. To form an end lap, determine the length of the joint needed, and make a crosscut halfway through the log at this point, straight down across the grain. Now make a rip cut in from the end of the log. If the chain begins to bind, stop the chain saw and insert wedges into the kerf. Two end laps cut in this manner can be spiked together to form a continuous log. However, never load a lap joint with excess weight.

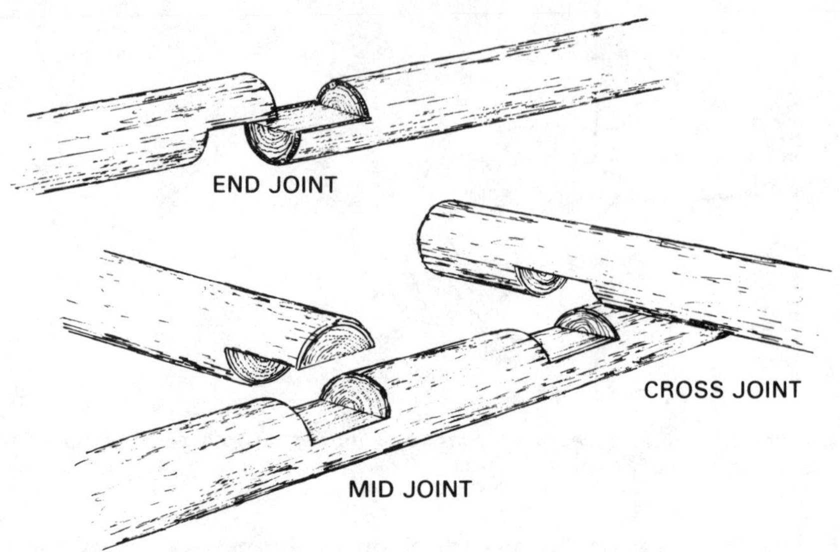

Fig. 6-6: Common lap joints.

Mid- or cross-lap joints combine two crosscuts with a boring cut. The result, a flat notch or joint (Fig. 6-7) in the body of the log, is one of the fastest and easiest ways of jointing logs together.

Fig. 6-7: A lap joint made by "walking" the saw across in successive cuts to obtain the required width.

Corner Notching

There are a number of "log cabin" corner notching techniques (Fig. 6-8). Round notching results in the finest notch, because the shape of the notch prevents water collection. It is also the most difficult of the corner notching techniques. The notch must be carefully cut and fitted into place.

The width of a round notch is determined by the diameter of the log that will rest in the notch. Mark the width with chalk, and make a V cut between the marks. Clean out the notch a little at a time with an axe, hatchet, or wood knife.

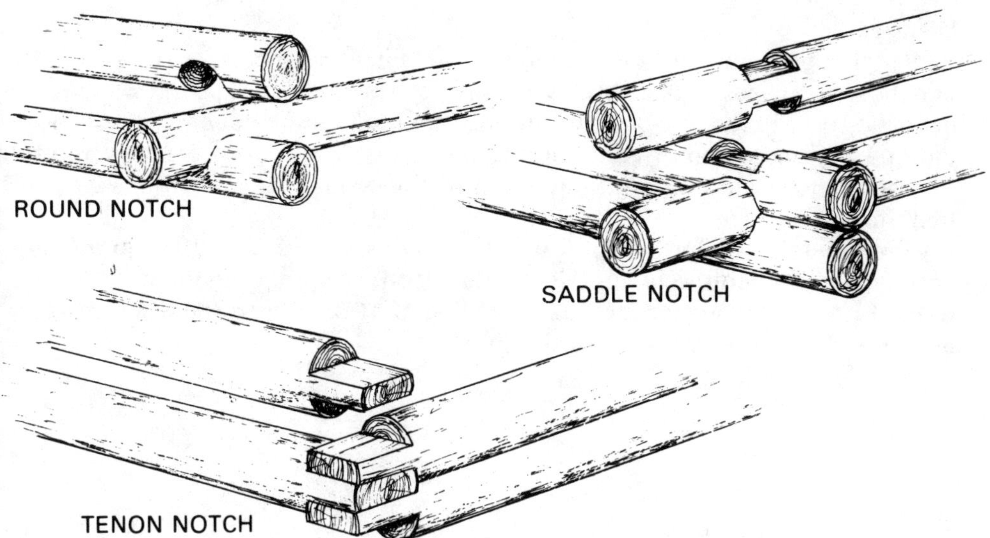

Fig. 6-8: Common corner notches.

Frequently check the fit of the notch with the next log. The final depth of the notch should be one half of the next log's diameter. The sides of the notch should have an outward slope to facilitate water runoff.

Saddle notches are much quicker and easier to make. Form saddle notches by making two shallow cross-lap cuts opposite each other on the log. Each notch should take out one third of the log, leaving a center piece with two flat faces. Saddle notches are the easiest and surest means of joining logs with a minimum of air space. All saddle notches must be protected with a wood preservative, however, since they are subject to decay from water accumulation and must be protected with wood preservatives.

Tenon notches require a crosscut one-third of the way through the log and a rip cut in from the log end. Little or no refitting will be necessary if you take the notch measurements carefully. Since tenon notches are also subject to decay from water accumulation, they must be protected with a suitable wood preservative.

Splicing Logs

A log should be spliced only if no strain is to be placed on the log. The rip should be twice the diameter of the logs being spliced. Spike in four places, as illustrated in Fig. 6-9.

Fig. 6-9: How logs can be spliced.

Wedges

Wedging presents an easy way to secure legs and supports to tables, chairs, benches, and other articles built with your chain saw. For exposed wedges, for example, drill holes completely through the piece to be supported, notch the tapered leg ends, and drive them into the holes. Then, drive wedges into the exposed notches to tighten the joints. Cut the excess leg and wedge ends off flush to the surface.

When installing blind wedges, drill the holes only partially through the supported piece. Notch the tapered leg ends, place the wedges in the notches (Fig. 6-10A), and drive the legs into the holes (Fig. 6-10B). Blind wedges force the leg ends tightly against the sides of the hole.

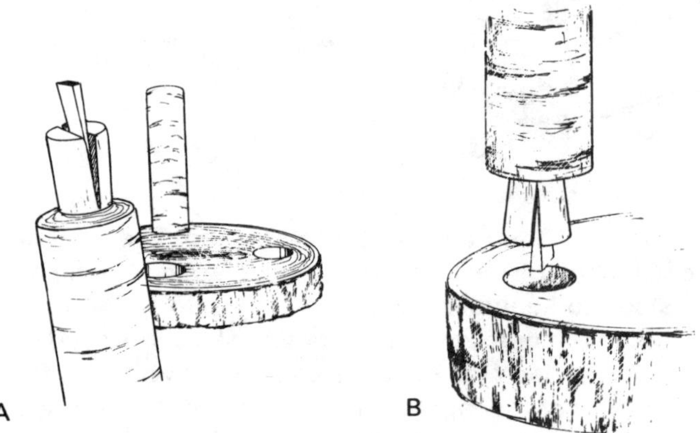

Fig. 6-10: How wedges are used to hold legs.

WOOD PRESERVATIVES

Wood can be protected from attack by decaying fungi, harmful insects, and marine borers. Of course, certain woods, such as cedar, cypress, and redwood, are more resistant to decay and insect attack than others, because the heartwood contains chemicals which are poisonous to fungi. Sapwood is generally not as resistant to decay as heartwood but absorbs wood preservatives better.

Chemical preservatives, which poison the food supply of the fungi and give wood resistance to insect attack, are frequently used to treat the more susceptible woods. There are two general classes: oils, such as creosote and petroleum solution of pentachlorophenol (Penta); and waterborne salts that are applied as water solutions.

For maximum protection, treat the wood after all shaping and cutting is finished and prior to assembly. Most wood preservatives may be applied to your chain saw project by brush or spray.

All dimensions for the projects in Chapters 7 and 8 are given in English measurements. A chart for metric conversion is given on page 152.

Log Projects for In and Around the Home 7

There are many projects which can be constructed of logs that can be used to beautify and benefit your home or vacation place. The rustic appearance of log articles fits well with certain decor, and the simplicity of log construction makes them easy to build. Remember that the plans given in this chapter and the next are intended to give your imagination a nudge and start you thinking of ways a chain saw could add to your pleasure.

INDOOR/OUTDOOR RUSTIC FURNITURE

Rustic log furniture inside or out will add more than anything else to the artistry and homelike atmosphere of a vacation home. Or, it is ideal for a child's bedroom, a recreation room, den, patio, or garden of your all-year-round home. It is by no means difficult to build, because every piece of natural wood has graceful lines. However roughly fashioned, you will find that your articles of furniture will be good-looking. In addition to the chain saw, you need some rope, some bolts, a few nails, a good sharp axe, a drill for boring holes, a draw shave, and few other hand tools, plus a few small logs and a little ingenuity.

In the eastern United States, birch is preferred as a material, and in the western section of the country, lodgepole pine is most satisfactory. However, almost any hardwood reasonably free from knots will do just as well. The lumber can generally be obtained by searching the woods in your vicinity for the proper type, shape, and size. In cities, such logs can generally be secured from fuel dealers in 4 foot lengths. Because green wood shrinks considerably—and this would result in loose joints—only seasoned wood should be used except where sticks or branches are to be bent. These bent members should be curved around a form and left to season for a few weeks in a warm dry place. When using some softwoods, be sure that all pitch is removed.

In log furniture construction, it is better to use screws rather than nails, as screws are less likely to loosen and pull out. This is particularly true in regard to slats used as seats and backs where constant flexing of the slats tends to loosen the nails. Where countersunk screws are used, insert false wooden dowel-like plugs in preference to plastic wood to conceal the screw heads.

The bark may be left on or removed, depending on your own personal preferences. However, the entire piece of furniture should be protected by applying a coat or two of synthetic varnish (polyurethane) not only over the raw wood, but also over the bark to prevent moisture from seeping between it and the wood. If the log shows signs of insects, thoroughly brush the bark with a mixture of 3 parts of boiled linseed oil to 1 part of turpentine before applying the synthetic varnish.

For rustic effects when the bark is removed, the use of a stain of the following proportions gives a satisfactory appearance: 2 quarts turpentine, 2 quarts raw linseed oil, and 1 pint liquid drier, to which you add 1/2 pint of raw sienna, 1/2 pint of burnt umber, and a touch of burnt sienna. The top surfaces of tables, buffets, chests, and rawhide seats should have two coats of synthetic varnish in addition to the stain. Another interesting finish—available in a natural shade or colors—is obtained by using exterior type penetrating stains. Depending on the finish desired, a final coat of synthetic varnish may be applied.

Due to variation in the available log diameters, only overall and essential dimensions are included in the following explanations of rustic furniture. Diameters of the logs used should be selected according to the strain to which they are subjected.

Tables

It is possible to make a rugged dining table, such as shown in Fig. 7-1, from logs and slabs. First, make a tight saddle joint between the top supports (A and B) and the legs. The cross poles should be set in place to impale the legs tightly. Next, notch the center support (C) to set between the cross poles. The upper sur-

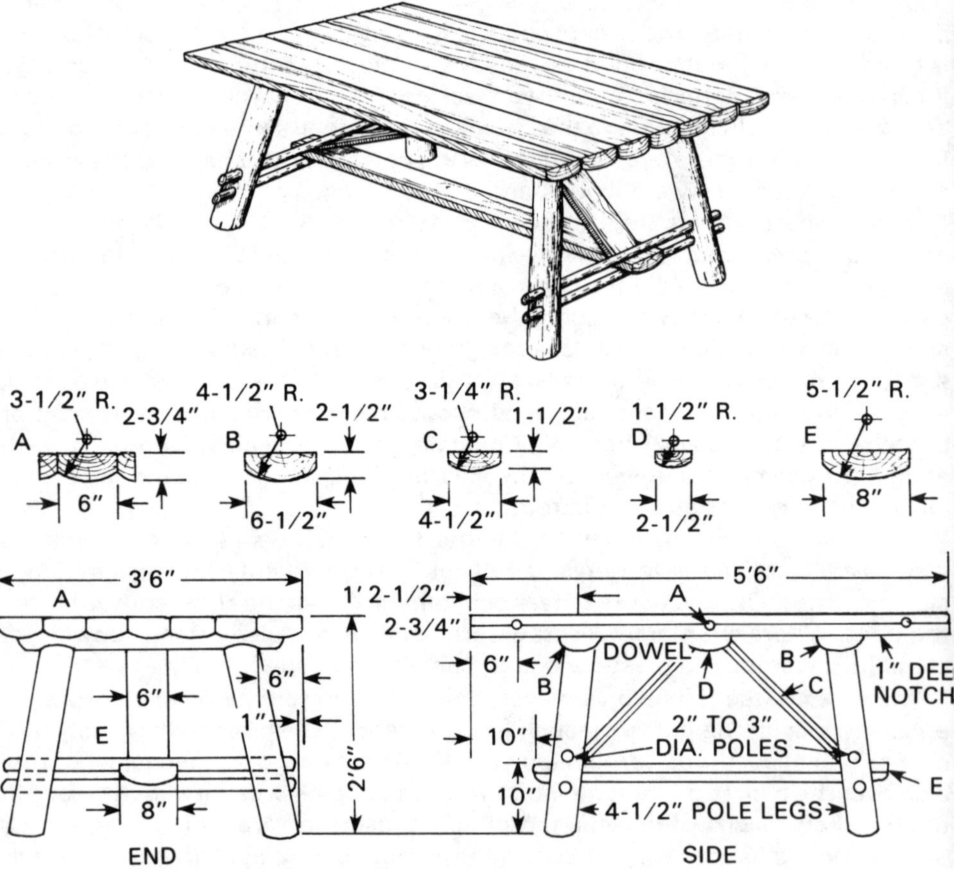

Fig. 7-1: Construction details of a rugged and serviceable rustic dining table.

face of the cross support (D) is fitted between the top support (E) and cross poles, all rigidly braced together. The table top pieces are then set on the top supports (A, B, and E), glued with waterproof glue, and screwed in place. The screws are driven through the slabs into the top supports and countersunk. The heads of the screws can be concealed with false wooden dowel-like plugs.

Three-Legged Tables and Stools

The three-legged table and stool have been American favorites for centuries—and with good reason. They always stand firmly, without rocking, even on an uneven surface. And, they can be beautiful as attested to by the oak burl slab table shown in Fig. 7-2.

Fig. 7-2: A three-legged rustic cocktail table.

Because it adds to the rustic effect, the bark has been left on the table, even though it may eventually peel off. The bark should not fall off, however, if the tree from which the table top has been taken is cut at the right time of the year. Unfortunately, this period varies from region to region. It is probably best to ask a local lumberman for the proper cutting time in each particular area. When working with green wood, it will probably be necessary to resand and refinish the top again after it dries. Therefore, it might be a good idea to rough sand the wood, coat it with boiled linseed oil, and let it air dry thoroughly before completing the table.

The legs can be made of rough hand-hewn lumber (as shown) or round logs. The small end of each leg may be turned on a lathe or may be whittled or hewn for a tight fit into the table top. That is, bore three 1-inch diameter holes, 1-1/2 inches deep at a 15-degree angle, approximately 5-1/2 inches from the edge of the table top bottom. Space the holes to form an equilateral triangle on the bottom as shown in Fig. 7-3A. Mount the legs with a wooden mallet. Cut the legs to a proper length and angle with a hand or back saw. A 17-inch table height was

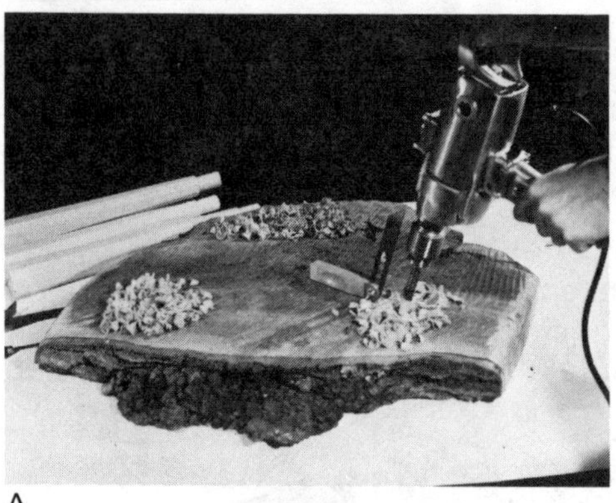
A

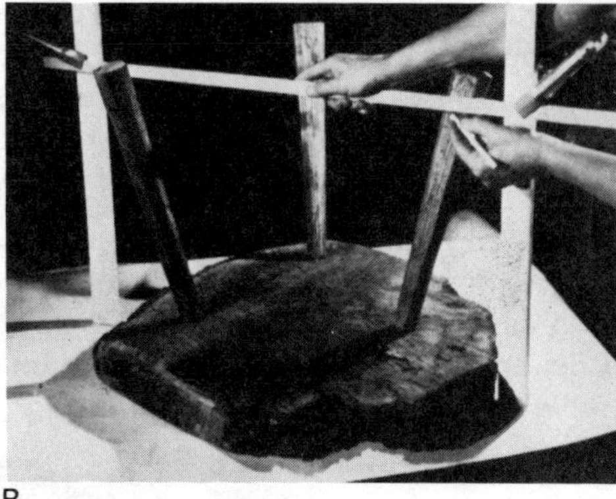
B

Fig. 7-3: (A) Drilling the holes in the table top for the legs. (B) Using a guide to level the table legs.

used for the table shown in Fig. 7-3B. Sand the bottom of each leg with a disk sander so they accurately conform to the floor. Chamfer the bottom corners of the legs with a spokeshave or block plane and install furniture glides.

Finish the table top with linseed oil. The legs can be stained with an oil-base black enamel, which should be applied sparingly with a cloth in spots and streaks to give an aged appearance. Then, before the enamel sets, apply an additional coat of dark oak stain with a cloth.

Figure 7-4 shows a design for a stool and end table that could be made from a slab. The surface sizes of slab depend on the diameter of available logs. The recommended measurements are: 30 to 36 inches for round table tops, 4 inches thick; 9 to 12 inches for round stools, 3 inches thick. When cutting slabs from log ends, use care to insure smooth surfaces and even thickness all around. Of course, when a log is cut in half, perpendicular to its length, a round section is formed. If the same log is cut on a diagonal, an elliptical section results, the shape determined by the length of the diagonal and the degree of angle between vertical and horizontal (Fig. 7-5). For example, a 24-inch diameter log, 48 inches long, will yield an elliptical "slab" more than 54 inches long by 24 inches at its widest points. If the guide of your saw is smaller than the desired slab, the two-cut method illustrated in Fig. 7-6 is recommended.

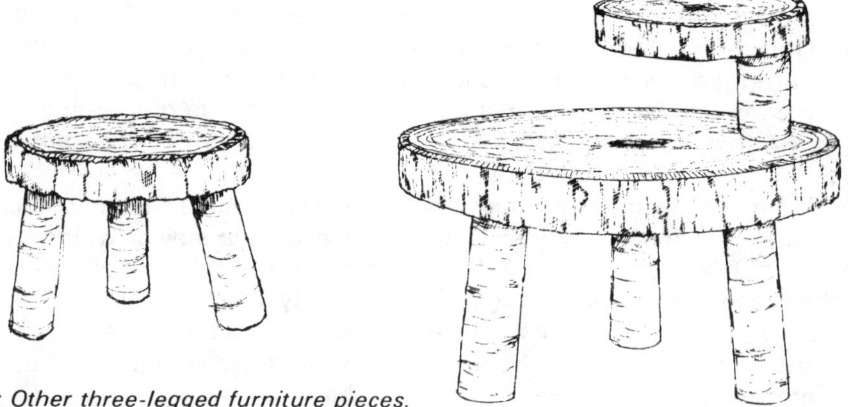

Fig. 7-4: Other three-legged furniture pieces.

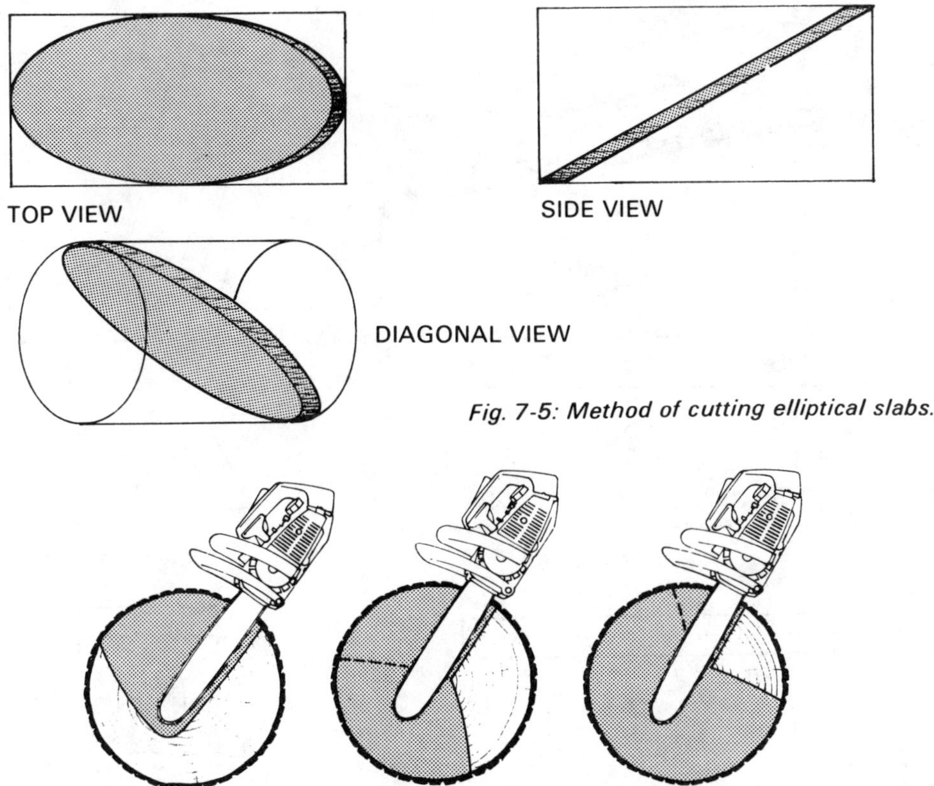

Fig. 7-5: Method of cutting elliptical slabs.

Fig. 7-6: Two-cut method of cutting slabs. When doing it, be on constant guard against kickback.

Benches

The bench shown in Fig. 7-7 is constructed like the three-legged tables and stools just described except that there are four legs and the top is a long, wide slab of hewn log.

The legs are set in holes bored in the logs. These holes should be about 2-1/2 inches deep and 1 inch in diameter. When boring holes remember the legs should have an outward play. The legs are made of 2-1/2 inch round stock with the upper end rounded off to fit the holes. Secure them as described in Chapter 6. The bottom stretchers are made of 2-inch stock with the ends finished off to fit into 1-inch holes bored in the legs.

If a back is desired, the holes for the back upright and arm supports are located and bored 1-1/4 inches in diameter and 1-1/2 inches deep. The stock for these members should be about 1-1/2 inches in diameter with the end of each piece rounded to fit the holes. The back stretchers and arms are set into 3/4-inch holes bored in the uprights. The arms are cut to size with one end rounded off to fit into the back upright. The arm supports fit into a 3/4-inch hole in the arm. The back stretchers are finished to fit into 3/4-inch holes. Screws are used to pin the joints.

Chairs

The armchair shown in Fig. 7-8 is simple in both construction and appearance. The corner pieces should be mortised and tenoned to the frame and rail and anchored in place with 3/8 by 6 inch lag screws. The arms should be fastened to

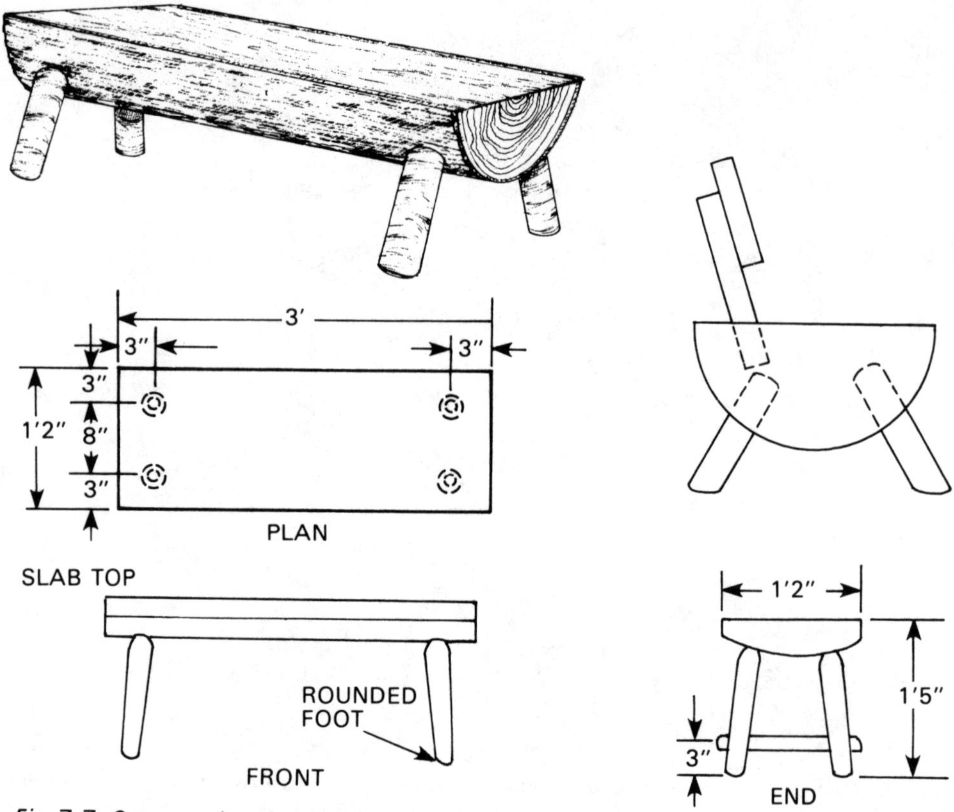

3′
3″
3″
3″
1′2″
8″
3″
PLAN
SLAB TOP
ROUNDED FOOT
FRONT
1′2″
1′5″
3″
END

Fig. 7-7: Construction details of a log bench.

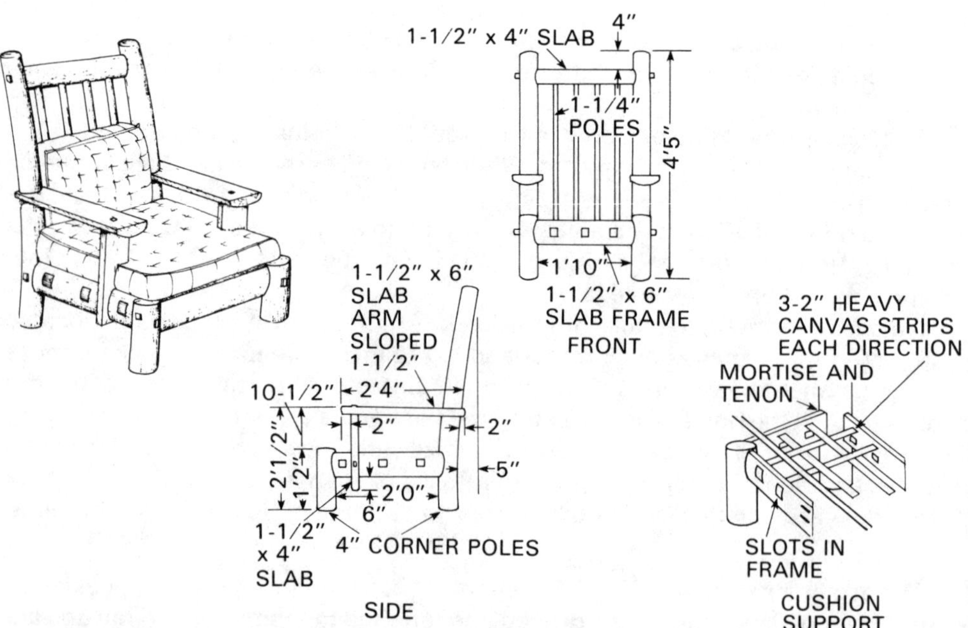

Fig. 7-8: Construction details of an attractive rustic armchair.

the corner pieces with 3/8 by 5 inch carriage bolts and to the slab support with 3/8 by 4 inch lag screws. The vertical slab support should be rigidly secured to the frame with 3/8 by 3 inch carriage bolts. Cushions may be of the filler type, without springs, and covered with fabric. Use 2-inch wide heavy canvas strips, securely fastened with furniture tacks, to support the cushions.

Upright chairs and stools (Fig. 7-9) can be made from the same material and finished as the armchair. Cross the poles to impale the legs rigidly. The cross-pieces of the chair back should be curved to fit the human back. The joints must be tightly glued, mortised, and tenoned.

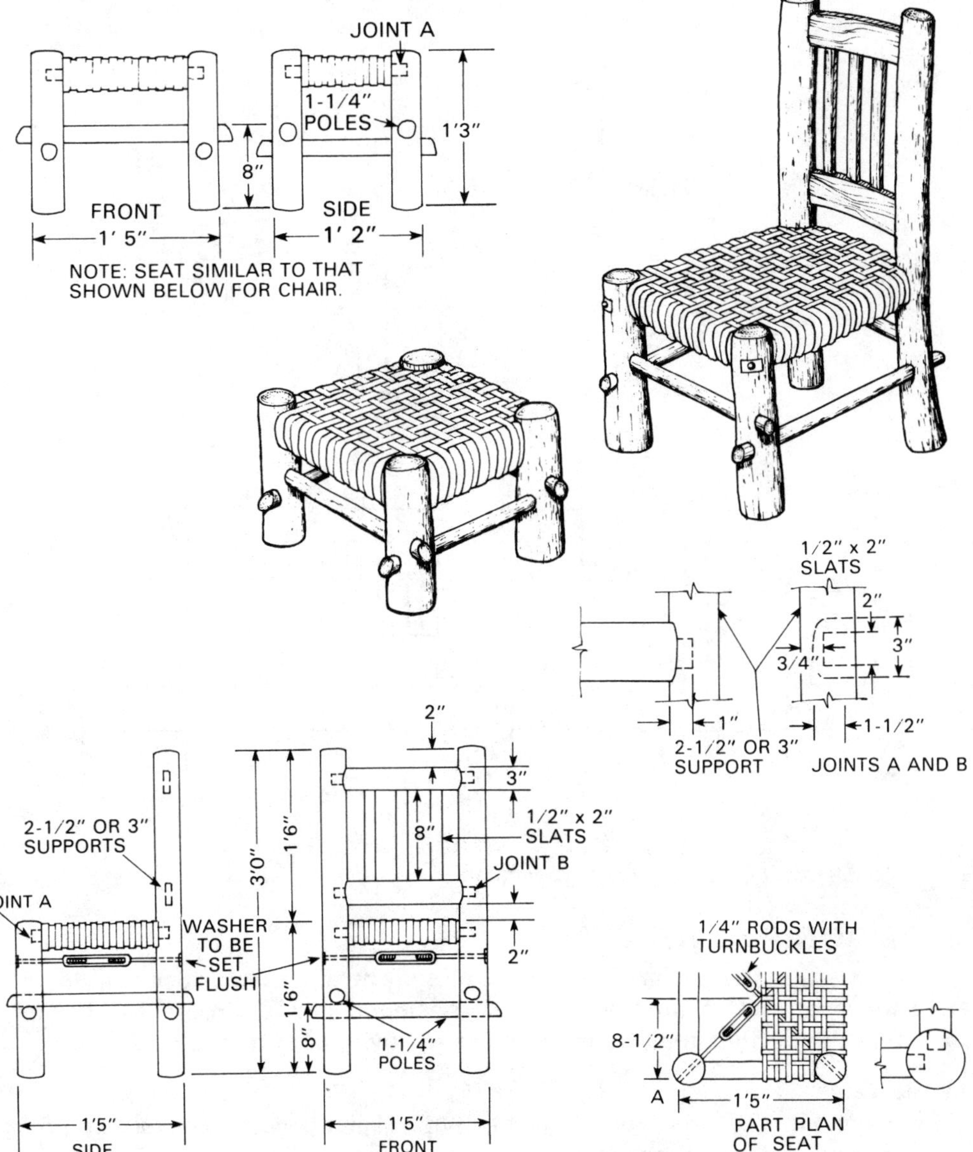

Fig. 7-9: Construction details of log chair and stool with rawhide seats.

Bed and Bunk

Birch or well-seasoned lodgepole or eastern pine is suitable for making a bed or bunk. In making a bed (Fig. 7-10), the crosspieces should impale the corner posts tightly; the joints should be glued and toe-nailed from below. Do not cut the side or end pieces until the bedspring has been measured, and then allow for a slight play in both directions in setting the angle irons, in order to facilitate the insertion and removal of the mattress. Use 1/4 by 3 inch carriage bolts to fasten the angle irons to the wood frame. Figure 7-10 is a plan for making a double bed; reduce the width accordingly for a single bed.

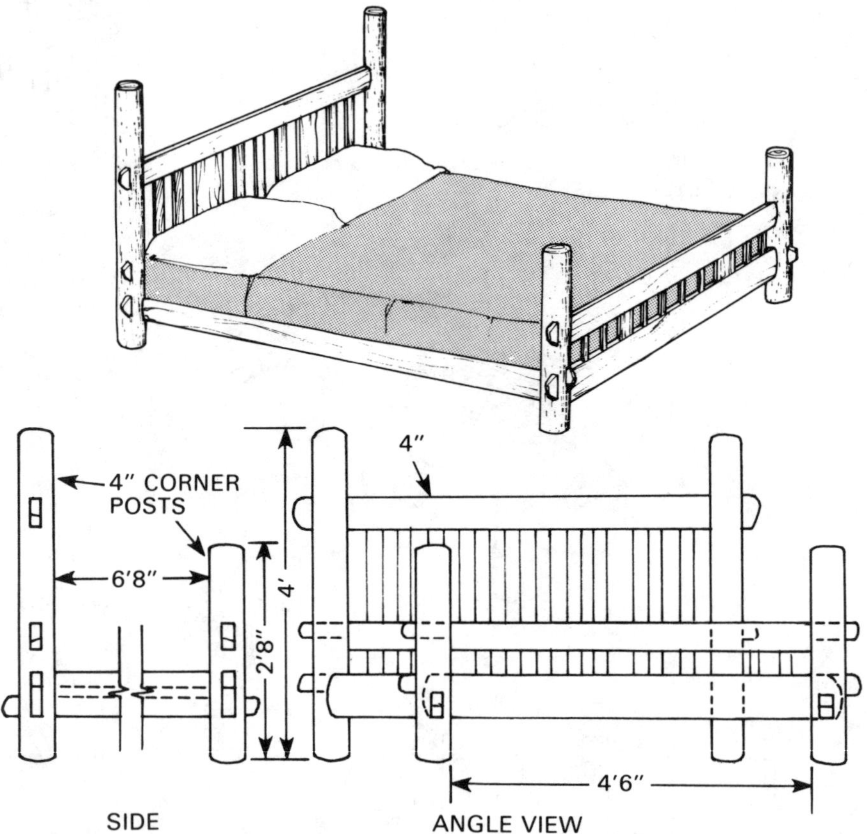

Fig. 7-10: Details of a simply made rustic bed.

OUTDOOR FURNITURE

While many of the log furniture pieces already detailed can be used outdoors, here are several items that are specifically designed for this purpose. Maybe one or two of the designs may fit into your patio, lawn, or garden plans.

Picnic Table

Shown in Fig. 7-11 is a simple log table that will give good service for any meal in your outdoor dining room. It is similar to the design shown in Fig. 7-1. Begin the construction by notching the legs and assembling them, using 1/4 by 5-1/2

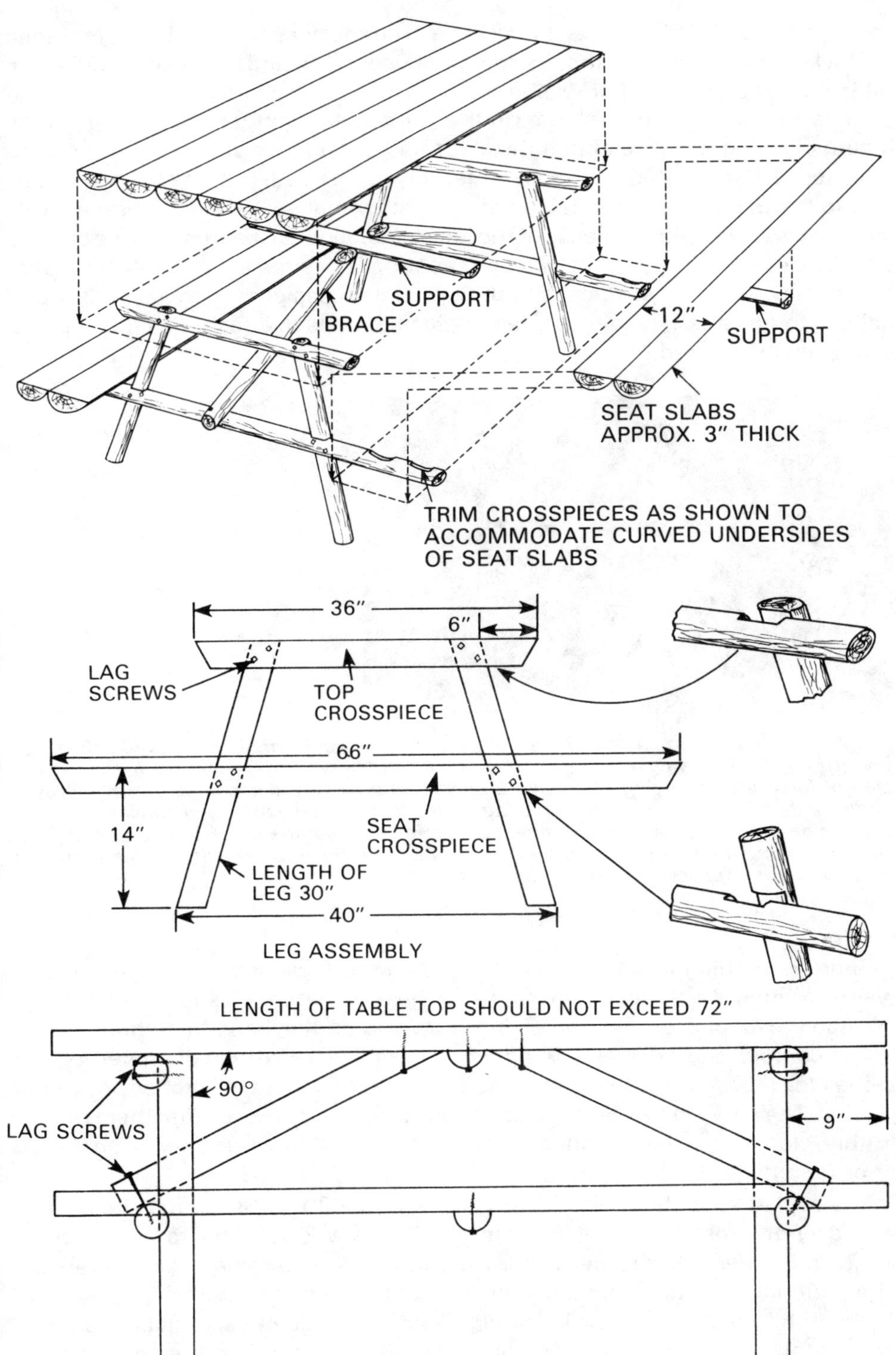

Fig. 7-11: Details of log picnic table.

inch lag screws. The lag screws may have to be shorter or longer if either thinner or thicker diameters than those shown are used. Drill undersized pilot holes for all lag screws and use flat washers.

Once the legs are assembled, rip the 6-inch diameter logs down the center lengthwise (Fig. 7-12) to obtain the slabs for the table top and seats. Attach the table top slabs with 20d box nails, preferably galvanized. Fasten the center support to the underside of the table with lag screws. Also, install the braces with lag screws. The top crosspieces of the leg assemblies can be trimmed, as can the crosspieces for the seat slabs, if a good seating is desired for the table top slabs.

Attach the top and seat slabs to their proper crosspieces with nails. Carriage bolts with flat washers can be used in place of nails to attach the table top and seat slabs, if desired.

Fig. 7-12: When ripping the top and seat slabs for the picnic table, use a sawbuck to support the log. Run the saw at approximately the angle shown and let the saw do the cutting. Do not force it by applying excessive pressure in an effort to speed up cutting. Draw a chalk guide line lengthwise along the log so that you will have two equal halves when the log has been ripped. Have assistance if possible. This is not a must, but can be of great help in guiding the saw by watching the underside of the log and calling out adjustments when the cut appears to be going off center.

Chairs

There is nothing like a cool drink and a comfortable seat in the shade on a warm, summery afternoon. The chairs and notch-seat bench shown in Fig. 7-13 are good examples of the type of furniture you can make with a chain saw.

The contour chair (Fig. 7-13A) is made from 20- to 24-inch diameter log, 36 inches (or more) in length. The front of the seat is about 17 inches above the ground. The curve of the "arms" cannot be cut in one stroke, so trim them roughly, then clean to the desired shape. Use chalk to mark the chair's shape on the log prior to cutting.

The bucket-seat chair (Fig. 7-13B) is cut from a 30- to 36-inch diameter log, with a length from 4 to 5 feet. Put a mark on the saw's guide bar to aid in making a consistent-depth boring cut. Slope the backrest at 15 degrees from the vertical. The main log is notched (about 6 inches) to fit the small log feet.

The notch-seat bench shown in Fig. 7-13C is made in essentially the same way as the bucket-seat chair except that it has no arms. Measure and mark the cuts, which are most easily made with the log secured in an upright position. Note the "rain notch" to help drain water from the slanted seat.

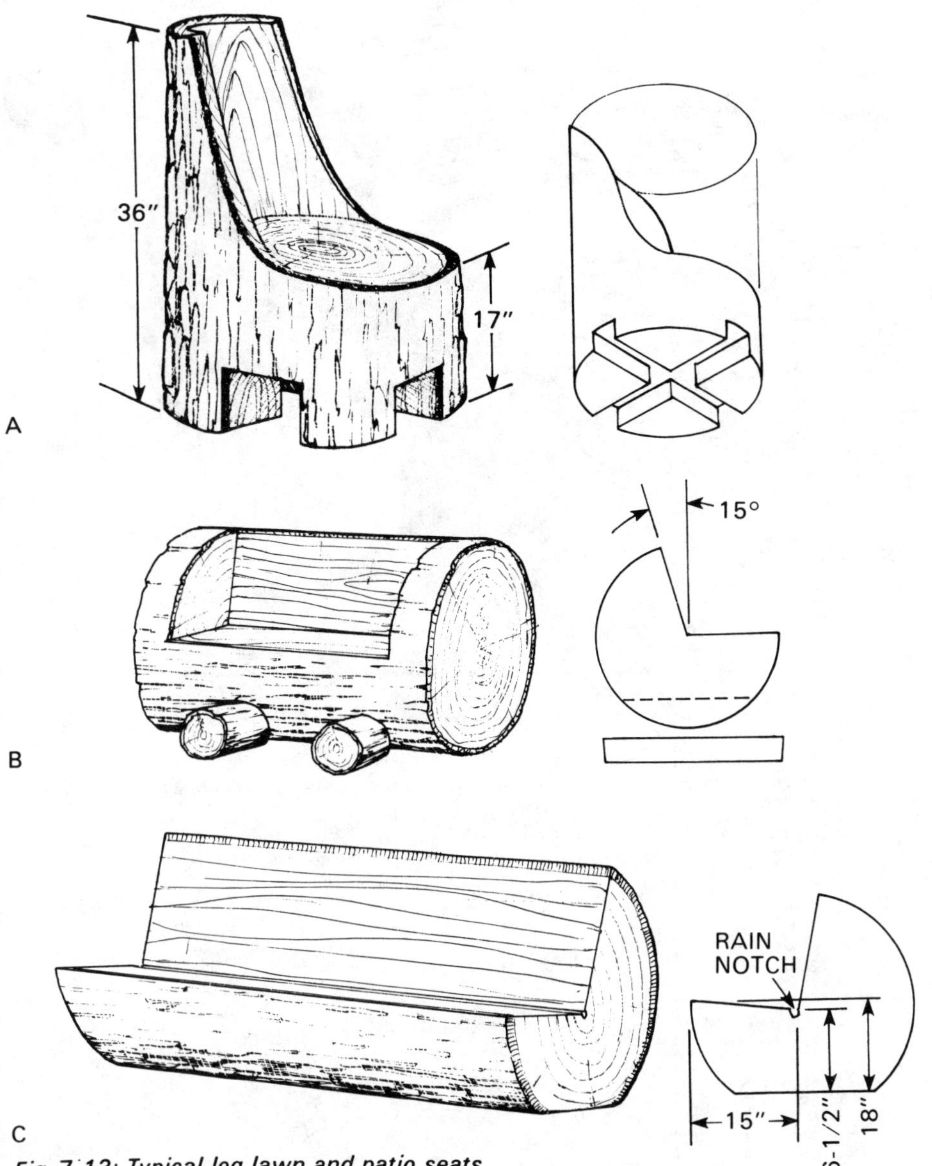

Fig. 7-13: Typical log lawn and patio seats.

Corner Bench

Before constructing the corner bench shown in Fig. 7-14, set its post in concrete to a depth of at least 12 inches. If the posts are not set in concrete, treat them with a wood preservative and set them at least 18 inches deep.

To assemble the bench itself, fasten the seat and back supports to the bench posts, using carriage bolts and lag screws. The corner seat support is a 6-inch diameter log ripped to provide a slab approximately 3-1/2 inches thick. The 3-inch thick slabs for the seat and back are ripped from 6-inch diameter logs and are attached to their supports with nails or carriage bolts.

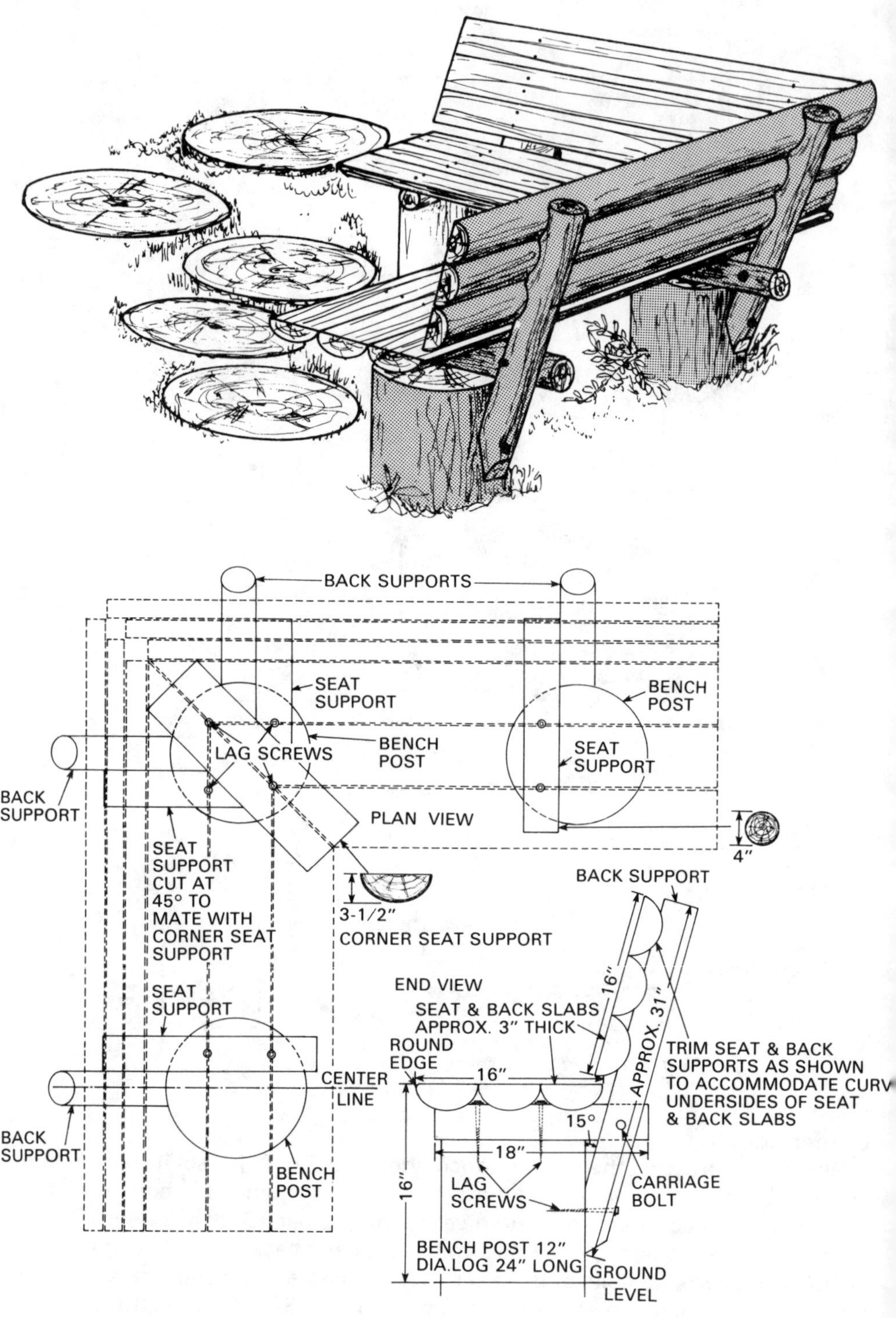

Fig. 7-14: Plans for a log corner bench.

LANDSCAPE DESIGN

The chain saw can help in making the landscape around your home more beautiful. For instance, the log rounds shown in Fig. 7-14 make intriguing paths in the traditional "stepping stone" style. Use them to lead admirers about your garden and to that corner bench in a shady spot for a long cool one.

Log rounds should be approximately 6 inches thick and cut from timber at least 10 inches in diameter. Mark the cuts with chalk, then make clean, parallel cuts for uniformity and smoothness. For variety, make elliptical disks by cutting at an angle (Fig. 7-15) or use disks of different diameters. After treating the round with wood preservative, position them in a bed of crushed rock or gravel and fill in between them with sand.

Fig. 7-15: Cutting elliptical disks to size.

Planter Boxes

Planter boxes are a custom feature in any landscaping scheme. For this reason, no specific dimensions are given in Fig. 7-16, only suggestions for designs that may be to your liking or may spark ideas for others that are closer to your desires.

Planter boxes are most effective when conceived on the grand scale so that the mellow richness of the rough sawn lumber and contrasting greenery can be used to full dramatic effect. They should most often be focal points in landscaping, and at other times will be found the perfect solution in filling a difficult area. All of the timber used in planter boxes should be treated with a wood preservative. All planter boxes that are simply laid on the ground should have a bed of sand or gravel to facilitate drainage. Holding logs together can be done with lag screws and spikes.

Mailbox Holders

When you are living in most country places, the postman does not ring twice; in fact, he does not even come close to your door. A mailbox that meets post office regulations must be placed at the roadside where the R.D. postman can reach it without getting out of his car. It is best to buy your mailbox ready-made, because they are approved to meet post office requirements. They are readily available in hardware stores and from mail order houses. The supports for the box can be homemade. Two easy-to-make styles are shown in Fig. 7-17. The

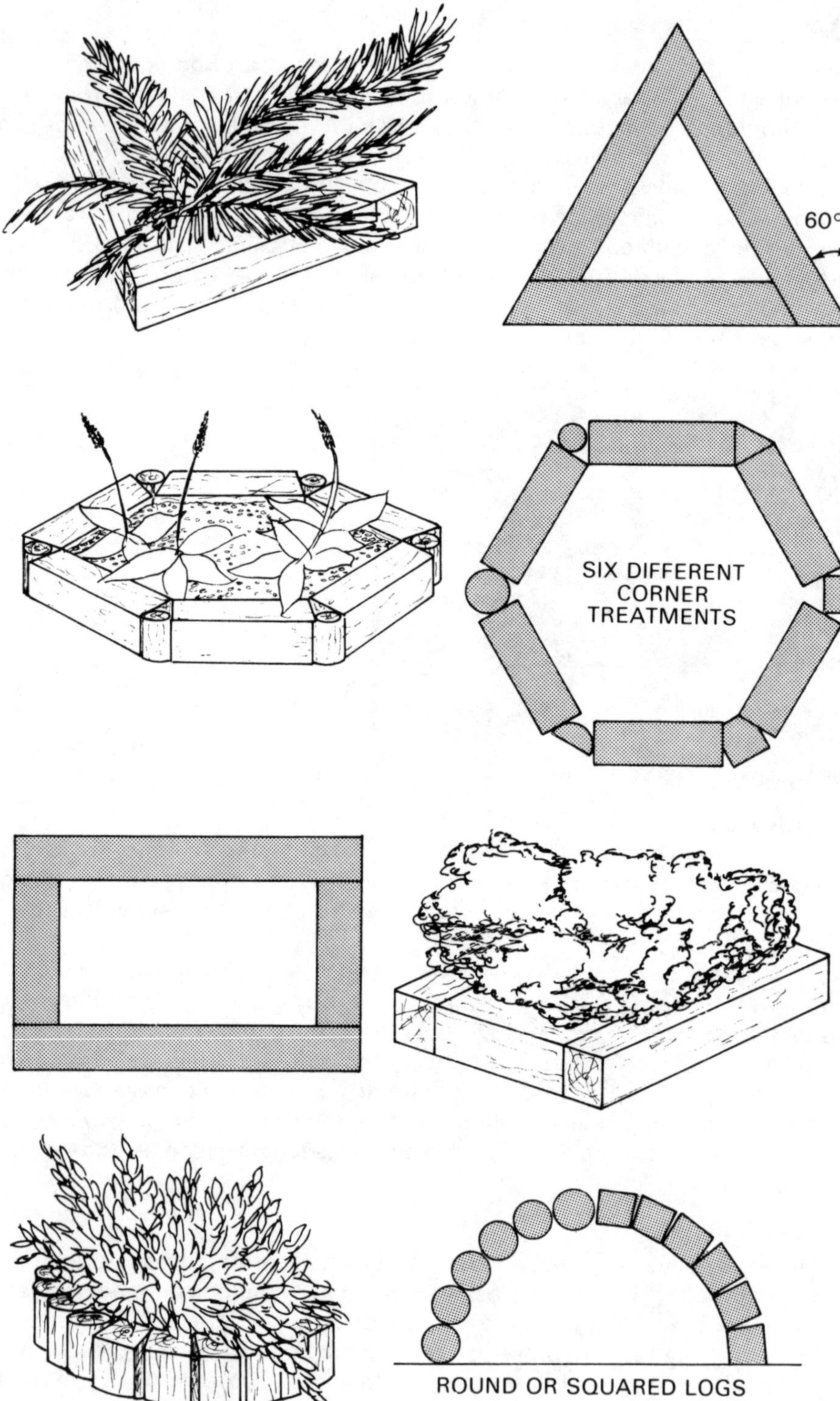

Fig. 7-16: Log planter box designs.

Fig. 7-17: Two types of mailbox holders.

post is usually placed so that the bottom of the box is from 3 feet, 6 inches to 4 feet above the road, but the exact dimensions should be checked with the local post office or with the mail carrier.

Fences

There are many styles and types of fences (Fig. 7-18); a description of them and the manner of their installation would fill many pages. The fence posts are usually 6 feet long. They are set 2 feet into the ground and are generally 4 to 6 inches at the butt end. The poles used for horizontal members should be from 2-1/2 to 3 inches in diameter and the crosspieces should be slightly smaller. It will be best to use posts treated to retard decay or decay-resistant posts of such wood as cedar or locust. They can be set directly into the ground. Setting posts in concrete is expensive and often does not retard decay. The sure way to prevent rot is to apply a wood preservative as described in Chapter 6. The wood should be thoroughly dry, and before this treatment, all bark should be peeled off the part of the post that is to go into the ground.

As a first step, figure out how many posts and rails you need. Then cut the logs to size. Lay the posts out on the ground to mark them. Then, with an axe, notch the posts for the rails. The only exception to this procedure is when the fence is to be set on a slope. Here it is necessary to make the notches at an angle so that the rails would parallel the ground and still permit the posts to be set vertically.

Next, stake out the locations for the posts and dig holes for them. Make the holes of a uniform depth and set the posts in position. Then, tamp the earth down well around them. The rails are set in the posts and fastened in place with nails. Keep checking with a carpenter's level as the rails are installed to make sure that the posts are plumb and the rails are level. After the posts and rails are set in place, the log pickets can be nailed in position.

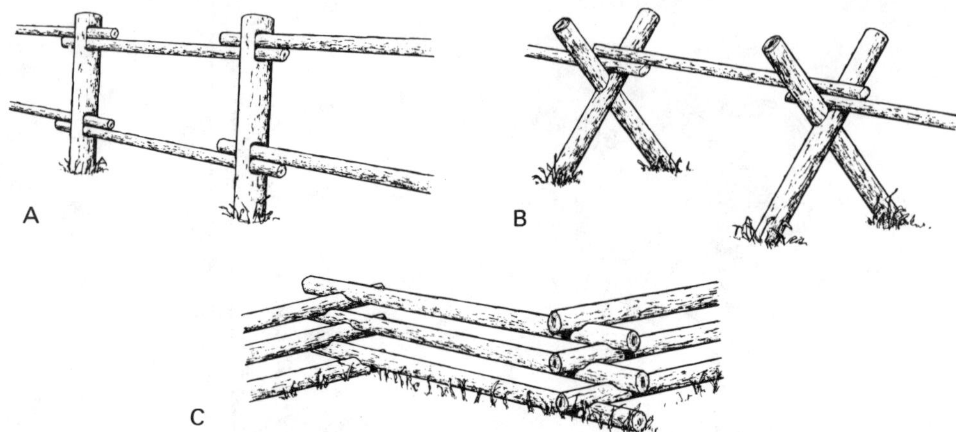

Fig. 7-18: Three common log fences: (A) With the mortise-post fence, the mortise can be carefully bored through the post using a chain saw. (B) The sawbuck fence posts are cross-lapped with the rail nailed to them. (C) With the zig-zag fence, the rails interlock where they meet at an angle and stand by themselves. One spike through each rail into the one below it is all the fastening needed.

Gates. A fence gate can be very simply made. It does not have to be next to a post but can be as much as 1 foot away. Such a gate consists of two log rails of the correct length, plus a log brace, pickets, gate hinges, and a fastener. Although a rustic fence and gate may look more picturesque if the bark is left on the logs, in many cases, this bark will soon begin to loosen and peel off. In addition, there is always the danger that insects may get under the bark. To keep the logs in good condition, scrape the loose bark off and brush on a mixture composed of 3 parts linseed oil and 1 part turpentine.

For those who wish, it is often possible to obtain rustic gates and fences fabricated in sections at your local lumber company. These require only the setting of posts and the attaching of the sections to the post.

Arbors. Rustic arbors may be made by following the same general instructions laid down for fences and gates. Start out with thick logs and end up with smaller ones. A much more pleasing design will be obtained by using lighter poles as one goes higher in height.

8 Outdoor Activities and Your Chain Saw

The chain saw is a great helper for the outdoor enthusiast. Whether your outdoor activities include swimming, boating, camping, skiing, fishing, hunting, or several of these sports, there are chain saw projects that will make them more fun. Of course, in some, the chain saw is part of the sport itself. For instance, the chain saw, in logging country, is frequently used as a deer hunting decoy. In such areas, the deer are conditioned to associate the sound of a chain saw with fresh browse. Where the deer have browsed beyond their reach, fresh trees and limbs represent a new and increased food supply. Also, since the deer have learned to equivocate the sound of a chain saw and the scent of humans as normal things in the woods, they become less wary and are easier to take when they hear the friendly sound of a chain saw.

Floats and Docks

For those who own property on a lake shore or water front and have a boat, a float and a dock are "musts." Floats may be built of old oil drums or logs. A standard 55-gallon drum will support approximately 400 pounds net weight. A number of them will provide ample flotation for any crosspieces and decking that may be built over them. For the swimming float shown in Fig. 8-1, five main poles provide the frame; lumber boards or small logs complete the float. Airtight steel drums or other containers (filled with styrene-foam, if possible) provide the flotation and are roped to the frame, one at each corner.

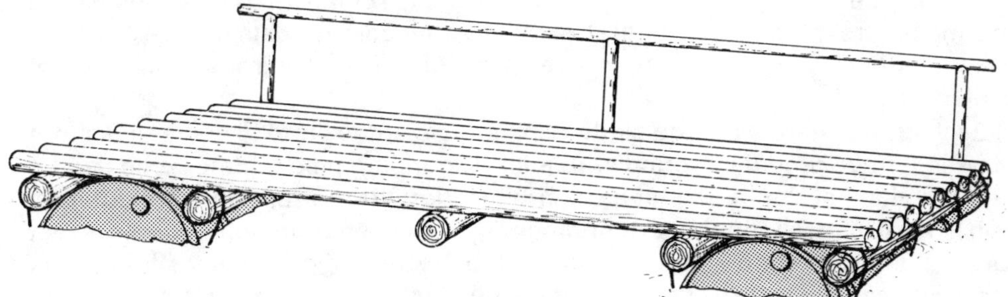

Fig. 8-1: A float like this makes a fine diving platform if anchored over a deep spot.

When drums or similar containers are not obtainable, logs or heavy timbers can be used in much the same way. No definite rule can be laid down as to their flotation because various woods will be used. The usual plan is to use lightweight woods and enough members to provide flotation well in excess of what is required. When logs or timbers are tied together and decked over for a simple

Fig. 8-2: Typical log raft.

float, it is easy to judge the flotation properties as the building progresses. As shown in Fig. 8-2, suitable length logs are locked together by cross braces notched and spiked (or bolted) to each log. Roping between the logs can give additional reinforcement. The log swimming float, if the anchorage is taken up, can become a log raft. When used for the latter purpose, only swimmers should be aboard, unless life-jacketed.

Smaller rivers, coves, and sheltered bays are best suited to permanent docks. Whatever the size or type of structure, the nature of the bottom must be considered, driven piling being suited to soft sand or mud but rock bottom making rock-filled cribbing necessary. Certain general principles of building apply to rock-filled cribs whether or not the dock is to take a boathouse. In case a boathouse is to be erected atop or alongside the dock, the formation in which the cribs are sunk will have to be made accordingly, but their construction and handling will be the same as for an ordinary dock, such as the one shown in Fig. 8-3.

Cedar is, in many sections, an easily secured wood for crib building; it lasts a long time in water and is easily worked and handled. White oak is another durable wood; because of its strength, members can be smaller than those of soft wood. Pine, fir, and other woods, especially when used for corner posts, should preferably be creosoted or treated with some preservative. In locations where marine borers infest the waters, sheathe the four corner posts of each crib from the water line down with sheet copper, zinc, or galvanized iron in this order of preference.

Each crib is merely a large slatted box to hold stones and is made up ashore after you have prodded around with a long sounding pole to determine depths and the slope of the bottom at each crib location. Corner uprights are cut for a crib in accordance with these soundings. The lower ends are left a couple of feet longer than necessary. They are pointed to let them dig into any silt over the rocks and so help keep the crib in place until filled. Stringers and clamps holding the heads of the posts are not fitted until later. No general rule as to size can be laid down, except that the larger the area of the crib, the greater its holding power. Corner or end cribs for the average dock will run 5 feet square, with intermediate or side cribs 3 by 5 feet.

The partially completed crib, preferably an end or a corner one, is floated to its correct position, upended to float erect; enough rocks are dropped in to offset its flotation. It can then be spotted accurately; more rocks are dropped in to sink it

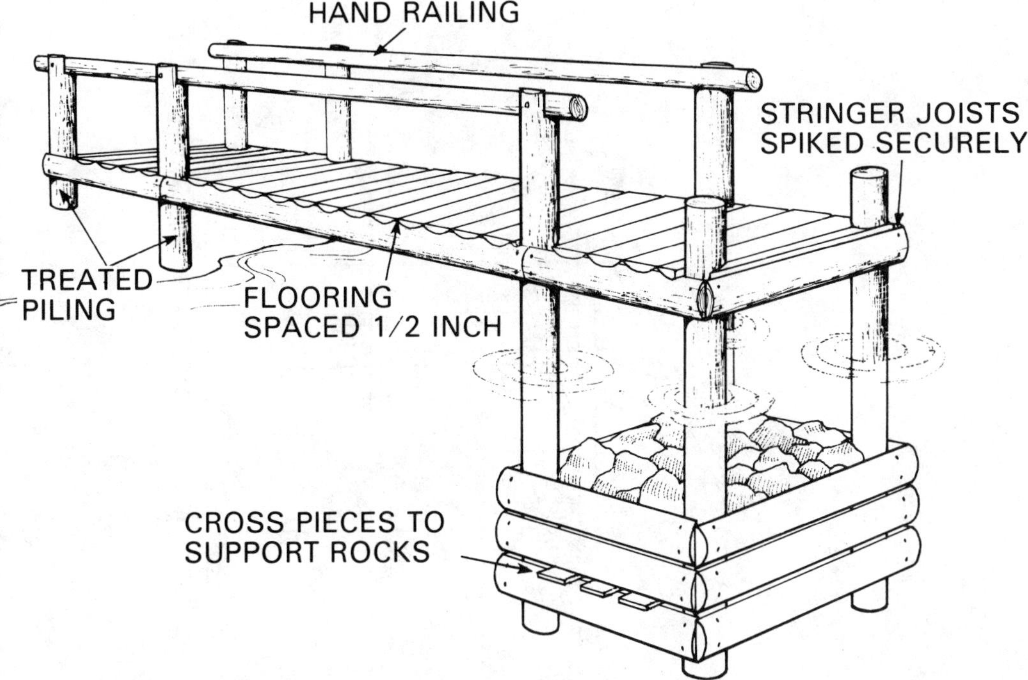

Fig. 8-3: A permanent type of dock with rock-filled crib.

into place. Every effort must be made to keep uprights plumb, corner posts being tapped firmly with a maul to do this. More rocks are dropped in, then lines stretched to stakes ashore, and to stakes out in the water if other corner cribs are required, to aid in locating them. Cribs inshore will naturally require shorter corner posts. When all cribs are in, temporary braces are nailed from one to another and filling is completed. These braces are left on until all crib uprights have been sawn off to the same level at dock. Cross pieces can then be let into their heads and long stringers fastened to the top of these to connect the cribs and take boards of the dock.

Duck Blind and Ice-Fishing Shed

Before leaving the subject of water-related projects that you can do best with your chain saw, let us consider the hunter and fisherman. If you are a duck hunter, the blind shown in Fig. 8-4 would be ideal. In shallow or sheltered water, this raised structure is built of light logs or poles for one or two men. The degree of "plushness" beyond log flooring is optional. The outer framework is designed to permit draping the exterior with camouflage material, preferably of native growth. Always strive for a natural, weathered look, so that it blends well with its surroundings. In fact, put the blind up well in advance of the duck season so that the "newness" will have worn off.

For the ice-fisherman, the log railed fishing shack or shed is simple to build, especially if you follow the basic log construction techniques discussed in Chapter 6. Observation of the various local construction methods employed by veterans of ice-fishing will help you in designing the best shack for your section of the country (Fig. 8-5).

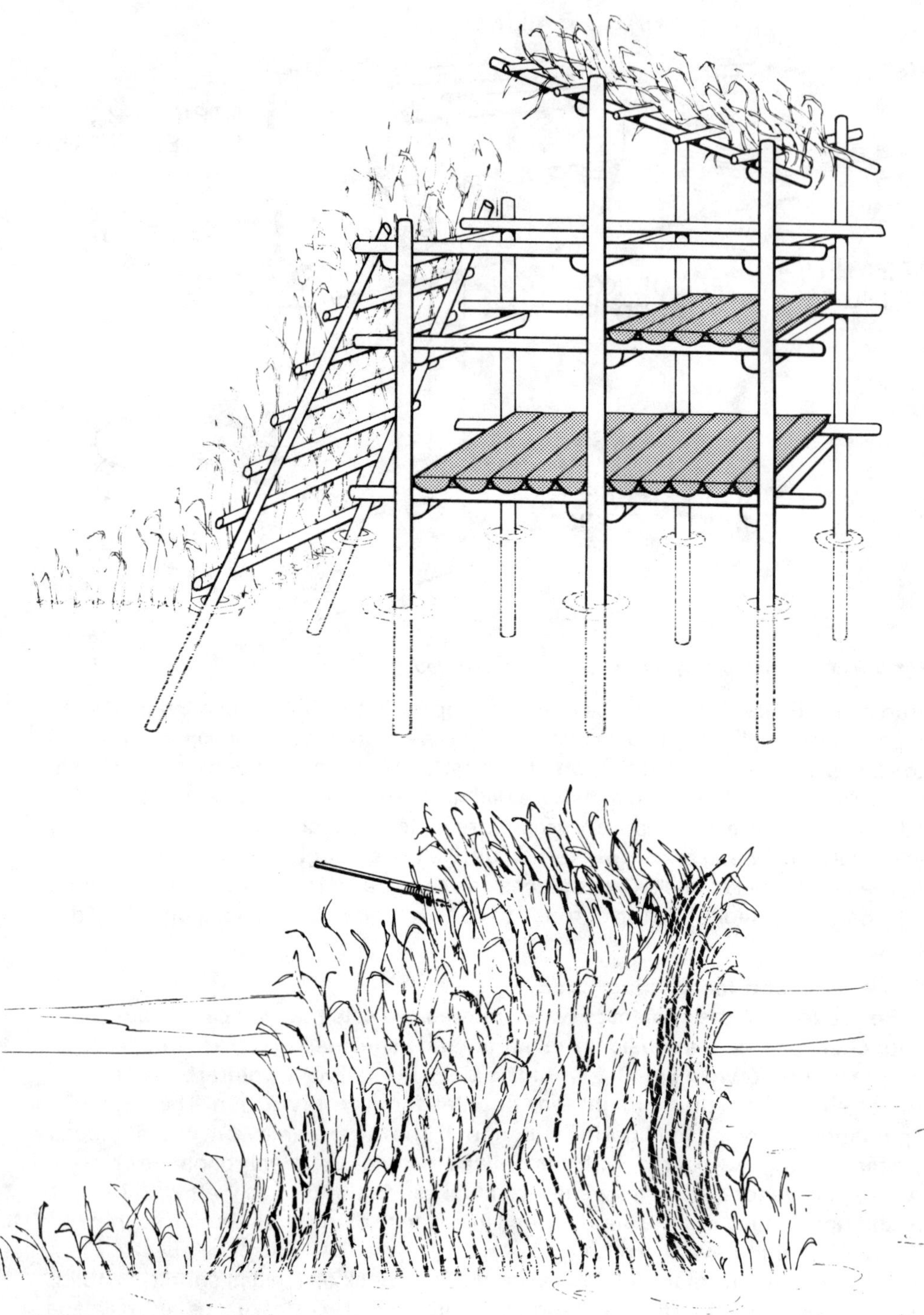

Fig. 8-4: Simple duck blind. Be sure the deck platform is high enough so that your boat can fit under it.

Fig. 8-5: Typical ice-fishing shack.

Log Cabin Structures

A chain saw simplifies log cabin construction by reducing the amount of work usually done with an axe. Larger projects, like the structure shown in Fig. 8-6, require help from at least one person, but the shelter shown in Fig. 8-7 should give no difficulty to one man. Incidentally, the latter structure is ideal as an overnight lean-to shelter for the camper or as a warming-hut rest-stop for the skier. And, it can be a backyard project for warm summer night sleepouts.

Fig. 8-6: Log cabins can be built for either year-round or vacation use.

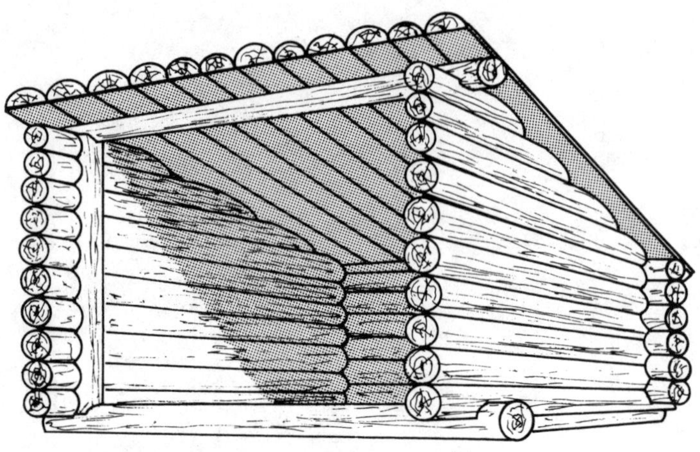

Fig. 8-7: Typical lean-to shelter. Size will depend upon its use.

The subject of building a log cabin for living purposes is too large a one for this book. However, the following are some important points to keep in mind if you plan to build your own log cabin. For example, a foundation should be considered that best meets the conditions in the area. If posts are used, they must be suitably treated with preservatives before setting. In cold country, they should extend below the frost line and rest on large flat stone, solid rock, or dense gravel. Concrete piers are probably a better choice for permanent structures, and can be cast on the site if hauling precast piers presents a problem. Continuous concrete footings for outside walls are strongly recommended. A concrete slab is an ideal base for any structure if availability, transportation, topography, soil characteristics, and temperature extremes permit. In log cabins, wood floors seem more in keeping, and are usually warmer to the touch than concrete. Tongue and groove 2 by 6 boards make excellent flooring even without a subfloor.

Roof type, pitch, and composition will depend upon the locality, weather, and aesthetics. All construction should meet accepted building practice minimums. Where heavy snows or other complications can be a factor, seek the advice of local builders, architects, etc. before beginning. Also, read the various reference books available on the subject of cabin building. Check your local library or book store. Also, remember that many home center dealers have a fine selection of books on construction and do-it-yourself subjects.

Chain Unit Maintenance 9

How you care for the chain, sprocket, and guide bar will greatly determine the kind of service you will get from your saw. Since the parts of the chain function as a unit, the breakdown or improper wear of any of these parts can have adverse effects on the cutting effectiveness of the whole chain saw. Improperly fitted or sharpened chains can cause rough, difficult, or uneven cutting, can put extra stress on engine, guide bar, or sprocket parts, or can even lead to chain breakage with the possibility of serious injury to the operator.

A clean, well lubricated saw chain sharpened correctly and set to the proper tension and cutting depth produces the easiest cutting and gives the longest and most trouble-free service. Remember, too, that dirt is the major enemy of sharp cutters. Never let a running chain touch the ground; it can become dulled instantly. Clean any mud or dirt off of the logs or trees before cutting. Also, make sure there are no metal items—nails, staples, gun shot, etc.—in the wood. Saw chains were designed to cut wood and only wood.

Saw Chain Parts

The basic parts of the saw chain were described in Chapter 1. However, attaining a thorough understanding of the parts of a saw chain and how they fit and work together is one of the first steps in proper chain care and maintenance. Let us again take a look at the standard type of saw chain.

The cutters, the most distinct part of the saw chain, have sharp points which stick up above the rest of the chain. There are four basic types of cutters on the market today. They are:

1. **Round or chipper type cutter** (Fig. 9-1A). The traditional chain cutter frequently found as "original" equipment on many consumers' saws. They are relatively easy to maintain with a round file of the proper diameter and a filing guide. The chipper cutter severs the same wood fiber several times as it passes through the wood.

2. **Chisel or square-shaped type cutter.** These cutters (Fig. 9-1B), which have sharp square corners rather than rounded ones, between the tops and sides of the cutting surfaces, sever the wood fiber with a single pass through the wood. Although full chisel teeth cut faster, filing of these usually calls for a special flat file with beveled edges, as well as a round file for cleaning out the gullets. They are somewhat more complicated and difficult to maintain than the chipper type. In recent years, a chisel type cutter has been developed that can be sharpened with a round file. While the round-filed tooth does not cut as fast, it does have the other characteristics of a full chisel cutter.

3. **Semi-square-shaped type cutter.** The semi-square cutter (Fig. 9-1C), or semi-chisel as it is sometimes called, is a compromise design—a semi-square

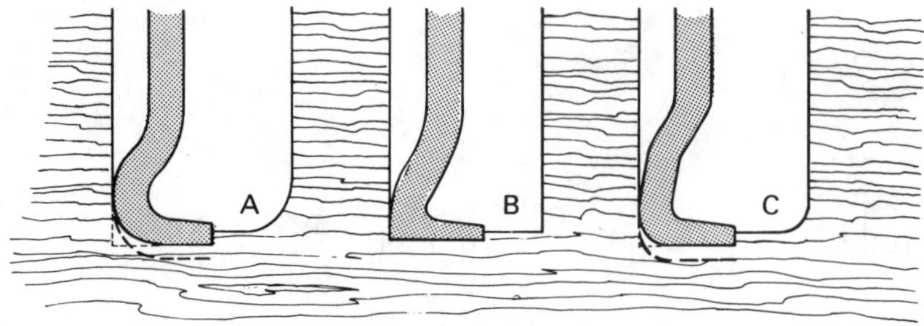

Fig. 9-1: Three types of saw chain cutters: (A) Round cutter, which cuts each grain several times; (B) square cutter, which cuts each grain once; and (C) semi-square cutter, which cuts each grain fewer times than the round cutter.

cutting surface that can be sharpened with a round file. Semi-square type cutters cut wood faster and smoother than round type cutters because they cut each wood fiber fewer times before the fiber is severed.

4. **Automatic-sharp type cutter.** This full-chisel cutter is designed to be sharpened with an automatic sharpener. The cutter itself has a distinctive claw-like shape that sticks up to allow the grinding stone in the automatic sharpener to reach the cutting edges.

Regardless of its type, each individual cutter can be broken down into various "separate" parts (Fig. 9-2A). For instance, each cutter has a top plate and a side plate which are sharpened to a fine edge and which regularly need resharpening to keep the chain at top performance. The outside surface of each top and side plate is usually given a hard chrome finish to keep the edges sharper longer.

The edges of the top plate and side plate are angled to pull the cutter into the wood. The edge of the top plate makes the bottom of the cut in the wood. The edges of the side plates make the width of the cut. When these edges are properly angled, the cutters are said to be "self-feeding" and are pulled into the wood automatically as they are pulled by the chain. To control the amount of wood the top plate can cut in one bite, each cutter has a finger-like projection at the front called a depth gauge. The relationship between the depth gauge and the cutter is important. The depth gauge must always be set lower than the cutting edge, but if it is set too low, it will be choked with wood and the chain will catch when cutting. In the same manner, a depth gauge set too high will retard easy cutting. Excessive sharpening of the cutters lowers them and necessitates the filing down and lowering of the depth gauges to keep the precise height relationship intact.

The gullet of the cutter is located between the depth gauge and the cutting edge. As the chain cuts its way through a piece of wood, the chips or bits of chiseled off wood are forced out of the cutter between the cutting edge and the rear side of the gullet. Clean the gullets of your saw chain with a round file before every fourth sharpening or so.

The base of each cutter has three working areas—the toe, the heel, and the notch. The toe at the front and the heel at the rear slide on the guide bar. They are also important in analyzing the cause of chain wear pattern, which is discussed later in this chapter. The notch provides clearance to allow the center or drive link to properly nest or fit between the teeth of the sprocket. Some small chains do not have a notch.

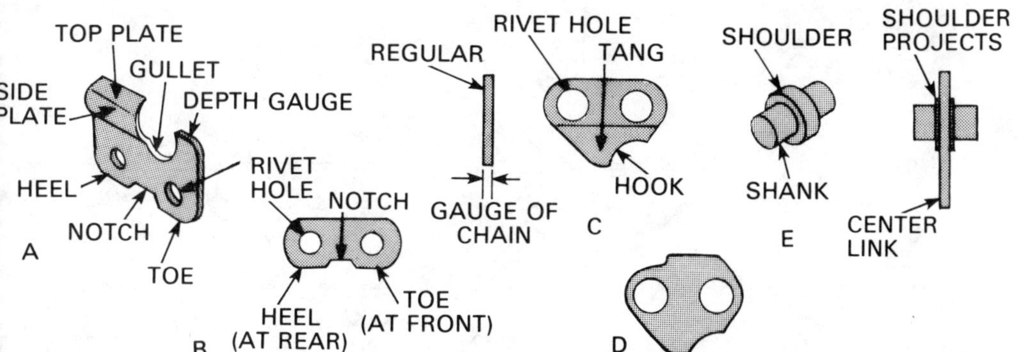

Fig. 9-2: Chain nomenclature: (A) Cutter; (B) side strap; (C) center or drive link; (D) center link of guard chain; and (E) rivet.

Side or tie straps (Fig. 9-2B), the pieces which link the rest of the chain and secure it together with rivets, are subject to great amounts of friction and wear from their constant contact with the guide bar. This friction makes the side straps of your saw chain especially prone to burrs and breakage, so examine these parts frequently and carefully. Remove slight burrs with a safety-edge file, pressing very lightly. Badly burred or peened tie straps can become tight and inflexible; and in these cases, the entire chain must be replaced.

The drive or center links of the saw chain (Fig. 9-2C), the parts sandwiched in between the two side straps of each link, function exactly as their name implies. As the crankshaft of the engine turns, it turns a sprocket or gear assembly, usually through a centrifugal clutch. This sprocket engages the drive links of the chain which, in turn, drives the entire chain assembly around the guide bar. The hook at the front edge of each drive link cleans the grooves of the guide bar. Clean this hook occasionally with a properly sized round file, taking care to maintain the original shape of the hook. In safety or guard chains, a guard link (Fig. 9-2D) is used in place of the drive link.

The rivets hold the chain together and act as bearings around which the drive or center links can turn. Rivets are manufactured with a thicker diameter center section called the shoulder or flange and two smaller diameter ends (Fig. 9-2E). The shoulder is wider than the thickness of the center link to prevent the cutters and side links from being clamped against the center links when the rivets are headed, thereby allowing the chain to be flexible. The two smaller diameter ends of the rivet are long enough to provide sufficient material for forming strong and effective rivet heads.

Types of Chain

There are several types of saw chains, the differences usually being in the shape of the side strap or center link, or in the amount of space between the cutters. As shown in Fig. 9-3, there are four different assembly patterns in general use.

The standard chain is assembled with one side link between each cutter (Fig. 9-3A). This is the most common assembly pattern. In large diameter timber, however, standard chain has a tendency to "hang up" in the cut because of the large number of chips which have to be carried out of the cut by the chain due to many cutters being in the wood at the same time. To provide extra space be-

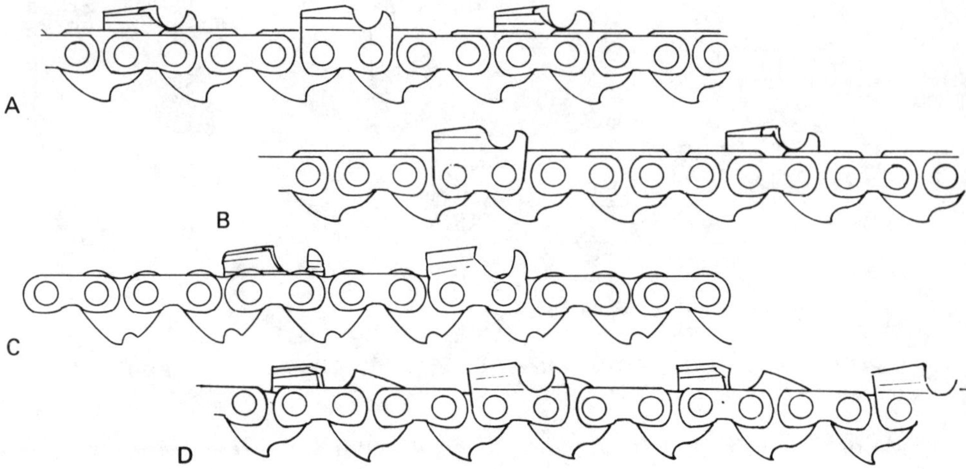

Fig. 9-3: Types of chains: (A) Standard chains; (B) skip tooth chain; (C) semi-skip tooth chain; and (D) safety or guard chain.

tween the cutters for additional *chain chip clearance*, the chain is assembled in skip tooth and semi-skip tooth patterns.

In the early days of chain saws, the cutting surfaces of the cutter were called the teeth and the cutter was often referred to as the tooth. This is where these two chains got their names. Skip tooth chain skips every other tooth or cutter and semi-skip tooth chain skips one out of every three teeth or cutters.

Skip tooth chain has two side links between each cutter (Fig. 9-3B). The extra space allows chips to be carried out of the cut much easier because the chances of recutting chips by close-following cutters is reduced. Skip tooth chain permits the use of longer bars on saws of the same power because only half as many cutters are in the wood at the same time. Because of the fewer teeth, skip tooth chain is rougher cutting than standard sequence or regular chain, and it is not recommended for limbing.

Semi-skip tooth chain has an alternating pattern of side links between the cutters (Fig. 9-3C). It is a combination of skip tooth and standard chain; that is, two side links between cutters followed by one side link between cutters and then repeated. It is smoother cutting than skip tooth but not as smooth as standard chain. It does, however, provide almost as much chain chip clearance as skip tooth chain and it makes limbing easier.

The safety chain is a special type of chain with a guard-type center link (Fig. 9-3D). This chain helps prevent small limbs or brush from contacting the leading edge of the depth gauges, which would cause kickback. Guard chain cuts somewhat slower in large diameter wood, but it is ideal for small diameter work. For most do-it-yourself woodcutters, the safety chain is a wise choice.

Ordering a New Chain. When ordering a new chain, the four items to check are:

1. **Pitch.** A common method of determining chain pitch is by measuring the distance between any three consecutive rivets in a straight line and dividing this

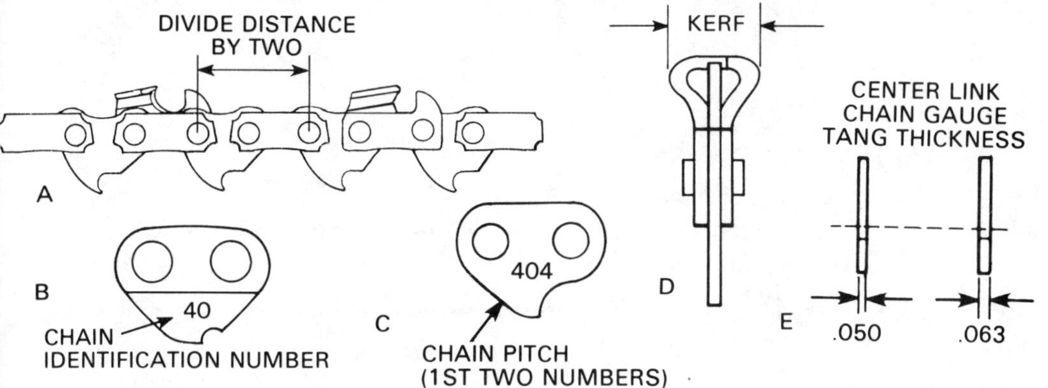

Fig. 9-4: Items that should be checked when ordering a new saw chain: Pitch, kerf, and gauge.

distance by two (Fig. 9-4A). However, the greater the amount of use and wear a chain has had, the less accurate this method becomes. Frequently, the pitch of a chain can usually be found stamped on the center link tangs of all saw chains except for the 1/4 inch (6.35 mm) pitch. As shown in Fig. 9-4B, the numbers identify the pitch, i.e., 40 means a .404 pitch. Where three numbers are employed, as in Fig. 9-4C, the first two are the pitch while the third refers to the gauge. On 1/4 inch (6.35 mm) pitch chains, the center link tang is too small to carry the marking. The absence of pitch data on the tang automatically identifies the chain as 1/4 inch (6.35 mm) pitch. Standard pitches are: 0.250 inch (6.35 mm), 0.354 inch (8.99 mm), 0.375 inch (9.52 mm), and 0.404 inch (10.26 mm). A few chain manufacturers stamp a code number on the center link rather than the pitch.

In general, woods with a soft, coarse grain can be cut best with larger pitch chains which can take bigger bites of wood. Among the woods easy to cut are pine, cedar, redwood, and cypress.

Wood with a fine, close grain structure is best cut with a smaller pitch chain because the chain takes smaller bites of wood. Hard-to-cut woods include oak, walnut, teak, ebony, ironwood, birch, elm, and maple. Pulpwood and woods used in general building construction are considered easy-to-cut woods. Woods used mainly for furniture and ornamentation, where the fine wood grain is important, are generally hard-to-cut woods. Frozen wood usually requires a smaller pitch chain.

2. **Kerf.** The kerf (Fig. 9-4D) is the width of the cut in the wood made by the saw chain. The smaller the pitch, the smaller the kerf. The best kerf for a chain is dependent on the power chain speed, length of its guide bar, and the size, hardness, and type of timber being cut. Saw chains are available with a kerf suitable for every combination of equipment and timber.

3. **Gauge.** Chain gauge is the thickness of the center link tang (Fig. 9-4E). It is one of the important "sizes" of chain. There are two major chain gauges in use today: 0.050 inch (1.27 mm) and 0.063 inch (1.6 mm). The gauge must match the width of the groove in the guide bar exactly. Normal wear makes it difficult to accurately measure the drive link thickness of a used chain. When buying or ordering a new saw chain, always use the number stamped on the center link of your old chain to assure correct gauge width.

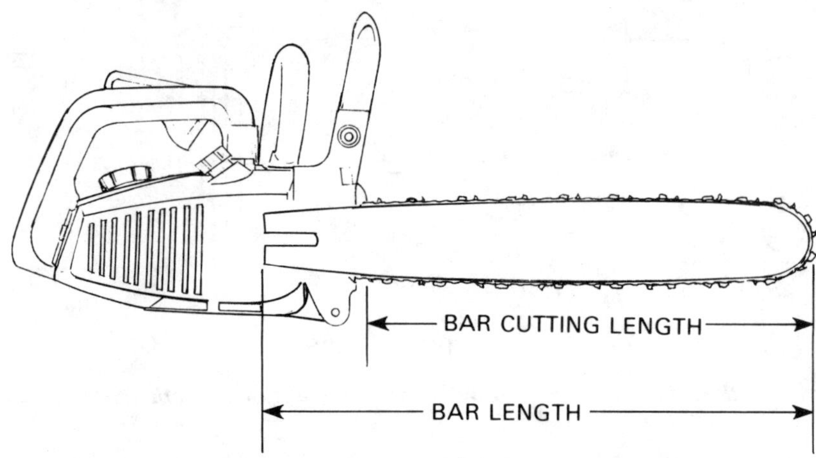

Fig. 9-5: How to measure the guide bar cutting length.

4. **Bar cutting length.** When ordering the correct chain for your saw, specifying the correct guide bar cutting length is essential. Figure 9-5 shows how to measure the exact guide bar cutting length of a saw.

Saw Chain Break-in. New saw chains require special care during their all important break-in period. All aspects of general chain care will be discussed in detail later in this chapter. But, since many chains are ruined within the first five minutes of their lives because they are pressed into service too quickly, here is a quick rundown on how to nurse your new saw chain through this dangerous period.

1. Check your sprocket for wear. If it is worn, replace it. A new sprocket is cheaper than the damage the old sprocket may do to your new chain.
2. Tighten the chain until you can feel a slight resistance when pulling it around the guide bar with your thumb and forefinger. Do not leave any slack around the bottom of the bar.
3. Run your new chain at no more than half throttle for a minimum of five minutes before trying any light cutting. Let the chain, bar, and sprocket have a chance to properly set themselves before putting them to work. Push the manual oiler button every 10 to 15 seconds to provide extra oil to the chain.
4. Make a few light cuts using plenty of chain oil for lubrication.
5. Watch your chain tension and retighten as the new chain reaches its greatest stretch during its first 30 operating minutes. Check the tension every 10 minutes for the first hour or so. In colder weather, the chain tension must be checked even more frequently due to the increased thermal contraction and expansion. When doing any checking of the saw chain, be sure to wear protective gloves.

Lubrication of Saw Chains

The most important point to remember concerning the lubrication of your saw chain is that it is virtually impossible to "over-oil" your chain. Plenty of chain lubricant translates into a longer, more productive life for your chain.

Before starting any size of cutting job, distribute a good amount of oil around the guide bar. Also, check the automatic and/or manual oiler on your saw to be sure it is full and working properly. Use the oiler often, especially when cutting abrasive woods. Remember, you can never waste oil, but you could ruin a good chain or guide bar. A properly lubricated chain will run cooler because there will be less friction between the bottoms of the side links and cutters and the rails of the bar. It will last long because there will be less elongation of the center link rivet holes by the rivets caused by friction. The elongation of the center link rivet holes causes the chain to "stretch" or grow longer and go out of pitch with the sprocket. This chain wear or stretch can quickly ruin a chain. As described in Chapter 2, be sure to use a good quality chain oil.

Chain Tension and Its Adjustment

As already mentioned, saw chains set at the proper tension cut faster and more efficiently. They also last longer and save you money. A chain set too loosely gives a slow, rough cut which quickly dulls the cutters. Slackness in the saw chain also hastens sprocket teeth, chain, and guide bar wear. A chain adjusted too tightly, however, can cause a number of serious and costly problems.

Check the tension of the chain before beginning and during any cutting job. Be sure that the ignition switch is turned off and that you are wearing good quality protective gloves whenever you plan on touching the saw chain. Always hold up the tip of the bar while making any tension adjustments. This prevents any shifting of the guide bar on its mount. To make the actual tension adjustments—when the chain is cold and hot—follow the instructions given in your owner's manual or procedures given in Chapters 2 and 3.

Chain Sharpening

While proper lubrication and tension are *very* important to maintaining the life of the saw's chain, keeping its cutters sharpened and correctly filed is the most obvious way of increasing the cutting load capacity and life span of the saw. Whenever the chain begins to cut more slowly, or the cutting becomes more difficult, it is time to check the cutters for sharpness. Sharp chains always produce solid, uniform-sized chips, so the appearance of fine sawdust is a sure sign that the cutters are dull or the depth gauges are too high.

Some chain saws come equipped with automatic chain sharpening devices which sharpen the top plates and set the depth gauges of the cutters as the chain is in motion. This reduces hand filing to a minimum, but does *not* eliminate it completely.

For saws without an automatic sharpening system, touch up sharpening with a file may be required once or twice during a day's woodcutting. In some areas, where sand or other abrasives have become embedded in the bark of trees, cutter teeth dull more rapidly and more frequent sharpening may be required.

Before sharpening any chain, examine it very closely and replace any broken parts as described later in this chapter. Sometimes, when the cutters hit hard objects, such as stone, nails, etc., or when they cut dirt, sand, etc., the tooth will be damaged and will require that this damage be filed away (Fig. 9-6A) before the tooth will cut or have the proper set. If one or more of the cutters have received damage that must be filed out, then all of the cutters must be filed back to that same length. The shortest cutter on the chain should serve as a guide when filing the others. To find the shortest cutter, measure the lengths of the top plate (Fig. 9-6B). The shorter the length of the top plate, the shorter the height of the

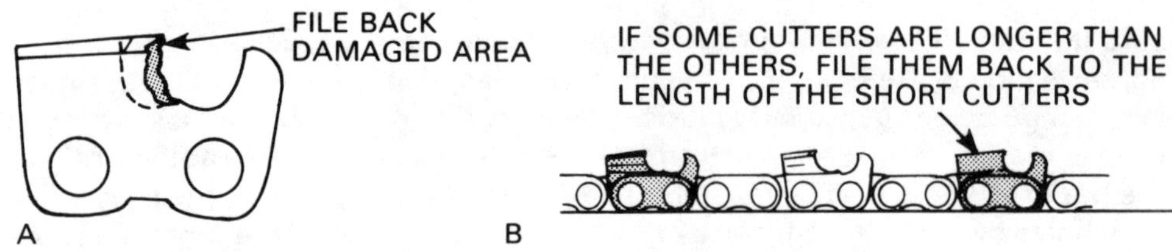

Fig. 9-6: Keep all cutters the same length after a damaged area is filed out.

cutter. While this filing back of all the top plates can be done by hand, it is less expensive and easier to have it done on an electric chain grinder by your chain dealer. Frequently, when only one or two cutters are shorter, it is easier to remove and/or replace them.

A chain filing vise holds the cutters extremely steady during filing, or the chain can be sharpened on the guide bar. With the latter technique, the chain must be adjusted to its correct tension on the guide bar. It is impossible to correctly sharpen a loose chain. If the saw is so equipped, the chain brake can be used to hold the chain in position for sharpening with the engine stopped. Carefully push the brake lever forward until it releases and the brake is engaged. The chain can also be sharpened on the saw by placing the guide bar in a bench vise while resting the saw on the bench.

Filing Equipment. Accuracy and uniformity are necessary for success in filing saw chains. These are easiest to obtain with the aid of a file guide (Fig. 9-7), which is set to the manufacturer's recommended top filing angle (some have an adjustable angle that permits several settings) and holds the file at the correct height to produce the required side plate angle and top plate cutting angle. Some clamp-on file holders have built-in vises which hold the chain while filing.

Be sure to use the correct size of file for your chain. Do not use any round file other than the one specified in the saw owner's manual. (If the manual is not available, check with an authorized service dealer.) A wrong size of file will hook or slope the cutters and will not let you get your money's worth from your chain.

Filing the Cutters. The dimensions and angles of various brands and types of chains may vary to a slight degree; thus, always check the owner's manual. In general, however, a top plate angle of 30 to 35 degrees (Fig. 9-8) will render the best overall performance of the saw and chain for most woods. The side plate angle may vary anywhere from 75 to 90 degrees, depending on the chain's design. The 60-degree filing angle at the top edge comes about automatically as you sharpen the top and side plates at their proper settings.

When using a file guide, hold it flush against the top plate on the cutter so the file is parallel to the top plate. (In the case of a round filed chisel type tooth, lower the file handle 10 degrees.) The guide automatically keeps 10 percent of the file diameter above the tooth. This alleviates the chances of filing unwanted hooks or back slopes into the tooth. Line up the guide mark on the holder with the centerline of the chain and steady the saw's guide bar so it will not move when the filing stroke is made. Then, hold the file at the correct top filing angle and apply pressure against the cutter, pushing the file towards the front outside corner of the tooth (Fig. 9-9), employing a rotating motion on the file. File in one direction only; move the file away from the tooth face on the return stroke.

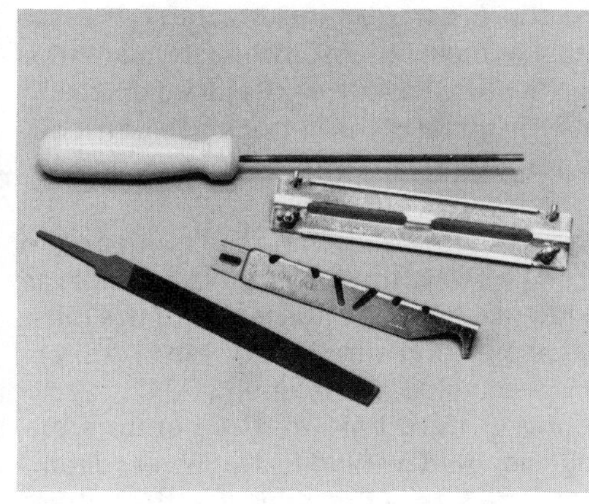

Fig. 9-7: Equipment needed to keep your chain in top condition.

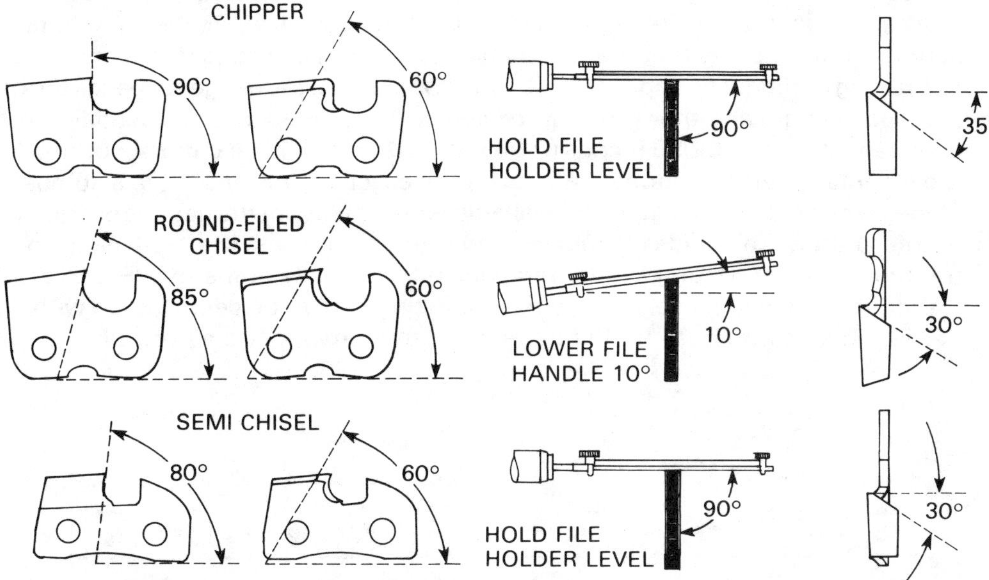

Fig. 9-8: Various cutter angles. When cutting frozen wood, the top plate angle can be reduced to 20 degrees from 30 to 35 degrees to remain sharp longer.

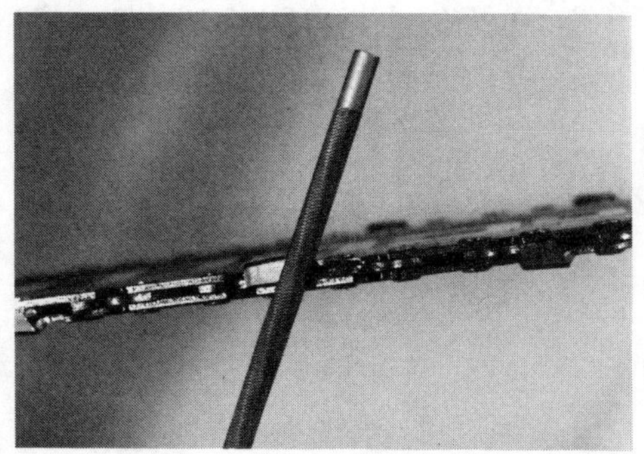

Fig. 9-9: The proper filing stroke.

Repeat the filing stroke until the tooth is sharp, using only a light, but firm pressure, mostly towards the back of the tooth. For most touch-up filing, two or three strokes should be adequate. Do not allow the file to dip or rock. Before completing the sharpening of a tooth, drop the file into the gullet of the cutter and clean it out with a few light strokes. When doing this, be careful not to touch the cutting edge of the tooth.

Sharpen all teeth on one side of the chain before sharpening the teeth on the other side. (This helps to hold the proper angle.) Use the same number of strokes on each tooth to keep all teeth the same length. Actually, this is one of the most difficult aspects of chain filing, since most people find it easier to file in one direction, ending up with the cutters longer on one side of the chain.

Lowering Depth Gauges. Every second or third time that the cutters are touched-up or sharpened, the depth gauges should be filed to the correct depth. As mentioned earlier, depth gauges control the size of the chips that the cutters can cut (Fig. 9-10). A tooth with a "high" gauge setting cannot bite, and a chain that cannot get a good bite requires too much feed pressure. On the other hand, setting gauges so low that the chain takes too large a bite causes it to grab and jerk during cutting. The depth at which you should keep the gauges depends upon the type of chain and the type of wood you cut. The depth settings usually vary between 0.025 and 0.035 inches (0.06 and 0.09 cm) for most cutters, but check the manufacturer's recommendations for the exact setting. There are a number of inexpensive depth gauge tools available which measure the gauges precisely and accurately. The guide tool fits over two cutter teeth with the depth gauge on the first cutter projecting through the desired clearance of the tool (Fig. 9-11).

With the guide in place, remove the projecting part of the depth gauge with a flat file. Take care not to hit the cutters or other chain parts as you file.

Fig. 9-10: Action of the cutter's depth gauges. If they are set too low, the results are erratic performance, waste of engine power, excessive heel wear, fast dulling, chain chatter, chain stretch, or breakage. If the depth gauges are set too high, the results could be slow cutting, fast dulling, and excessive wear of drive link and side link bottoms due to the pressure put on the bar by a frustrated operator.

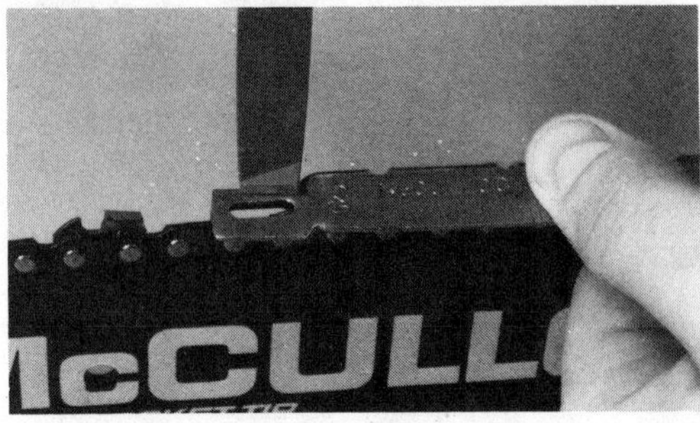

Fig. 9-11: Using a depth gauge guide and a flat file to lower a depth gauge.

After lowering all depth gauges, round off their leading edges, maintaining the same profile as on the original depth gauge (Fig. 9-12). Always place the depth gauge to be filed at the same place on the guide bar when lowering depth gauges. Since they do no cutting and only serve to determine the depth at which the cutters cut the wood, depth gauges do not need to be sharpened.

Fig. 9-12: Right and wrong way to lower depth gauges.

Whenever you adjust the depth gauges of the saw chain, examine the drive tangs or links as well. Chain drive tangs must have sharp points to clean sawdust from the guide bar groove and the bar groove must be deep enough all the way around the guide bar. If necessary, clear and lightly resharpen the drive tang with a small round file to restore the cleaning hook (Fig. 9-13). Be sure to maintain the precise original shape of the tangs. Remember, too, to keep the grooves of the guide bar clean as discussed later in this chapter.

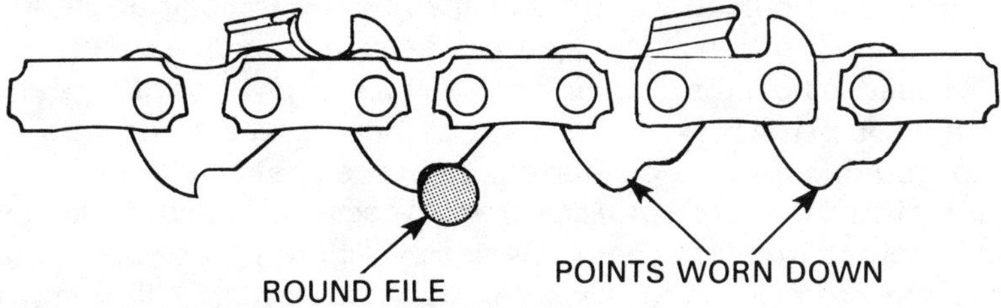

Fig. 9-13: Method of sharpening the drive link.

Cleaning the Chain. A chain should be cleaned after each sharpening to remove any filings which may have adhered to the oil on the chain. The filings can work their way between the moving surfaces of the chain parts and make portions of the chain stiff. A chain sharpened on the bar in the field can be cleaned by running the chain around the bar at a low speed while pumping plenty of oil onto the chain to flush the filings away.

The most effective cleaning requires removal of the chain and soaking in solvent or kerosene for several hours to loosen the pitch and resin. Scrub the chain with a soft fiber brush like a toothbrush and rinse the dirt, pitch, and resin away. Do not use a wire brush or you may damage the sharp edges of the cutters.

Cleaning the chain removes all the oil. Therefore, re-oil your chain as soon as you finish cleaning it.

Chain Touch-Up Filing for Saws with Automatic Sharpeners

As mentioned previously, some chain saws come equipped with built-in sharpening systems which sharpen the top plates and set depth gauges with a grinding stone while the chain is in motion. Methods of operating the sharpening stone vary according to the make of the saw, and it is best to refer to your operator's manual for specific details. However, the following operating points are common to most automatic sharpening systems.

1. Be sure the chain is properly tensioned before sharpening. With the engine off, remove any packed sawdust from inside the housing with a screwdriver.
2. When making a stone adjustment—with the engine running—turn the adjusting screw until sparks appear while the chain sharpens. This adjustment controls the amount of metal removed by grinding.
3. Most chains can be sharpened in this manner within a few seconds. If the cutters have been damaged by abrasion, they must be sharpened until the damaged area is removed.
4. The handle, knob, or other device must be operated through its full motion to insure sharpening of both right- and left-hand cutters.
5. Except when the actual sharpening is taking place, the grinding stone must be retracted so it does not touch the cutters.

Even on saws with automatic sharpening systems, side plate sharpening must be done by hand. In a typical automatic system this usually occurs when:

1. The side plate projects more than 1/16 inch (1.6 mm) ahead of the top plate (Fig. 9-14A).
2. The cutting edge of the side plate becomes rounded (Fig. 9-14B).

Also, it is usually necessary every third to fifth time top plates are sharpened and even more often when operating the saw under abrasive conditions. Take the same precautions you would in filing a saw chain without the grind stone system. Secure the chain firmly in place. Again, if the saw is equipped with a chain brake, it can be used to hold the chain in position for sharpening with the engine stopped. Carefully push the brake lever forward until it releases and the brake is engaged. Wear tough gloves whenever handling the chain.

Use a properly fitted file guide and a properly sized round file and file handle. These can be obtained from any chain saw dealer. Tighten the chain on the bar so it cannot lean over under filing pressure. After each cutter is filed, move the chain so that the cutters are always filed at the middle of the bar. Place the file guide on top of the cutter so that it rests on the top plate (Fig. 9-15) and the depth

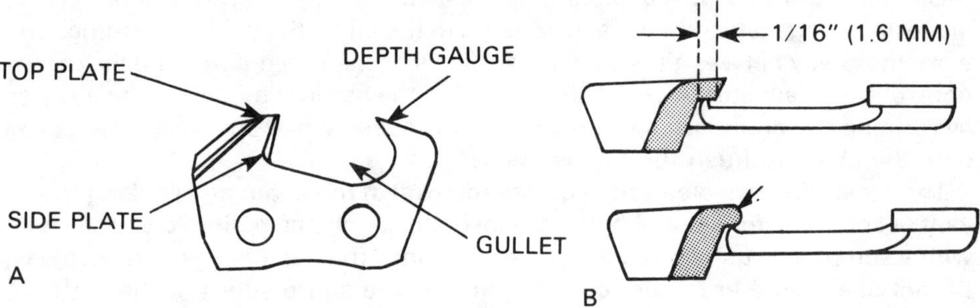

Fig. 9-14: When the cutters of a typical automatic sharpening system need touch-up.

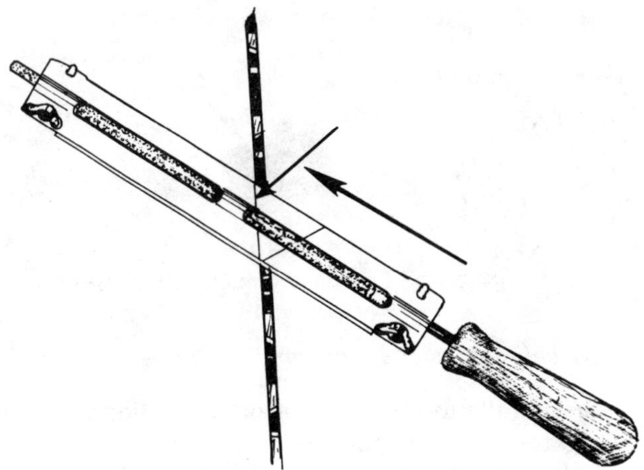

Fig. 9-15: Proper filing position.

gauge, and so that the guide line (usually at 22 degrees) on the guide is parallel to the chain; this insures a proper side plate angle. Hold the file level and never touch the top of the teeth with the file.

File from the inside of the cutter toward the outside, making light strokes forward and releasing pressure on the file on the back stroke until the edge of the side plate is sharp (Fig. 9-16A). Use the same number of filing strokes on each cutter. Always leave the side plate projecting ahead of the top plate (generally slightly more than 1/32 inch [.8 mm]), or the chain will not cut properly (Fig. 9-16B). If the side plate projection of your saw chain is less than 1/32 inch (.8 mm), the problem can be corrected by sharpening the chain with the saw's automatic grinding stone as described in Chapter 2.

Do the touch-up filing of all the cutters on one side of the chain before filing those on the other side. Never let the file cut into the chrome underside of the top plate. This will cause it to dull faster. But, always be sure to maintain the rounded front corner of the depth gauge.

Replacing a Grinding Stone in Automatic Sharpeners

The automatic sharpening systems on chain saws are designed to sharpen your chain until you can no longer adjust the knob without having it separate from the assembly (Fig. 9-17). When this occurs, it is time to replace the grinding stone. Most manufacturers also recommend installing a new grinding stone

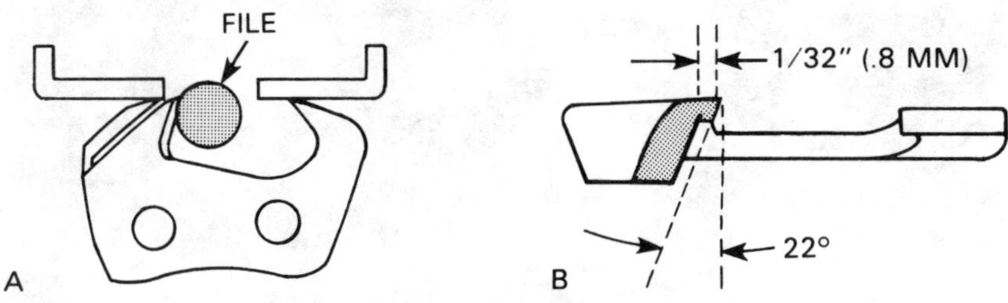

Fig. 9-16: Proper tooth shape must be maintained while filing.

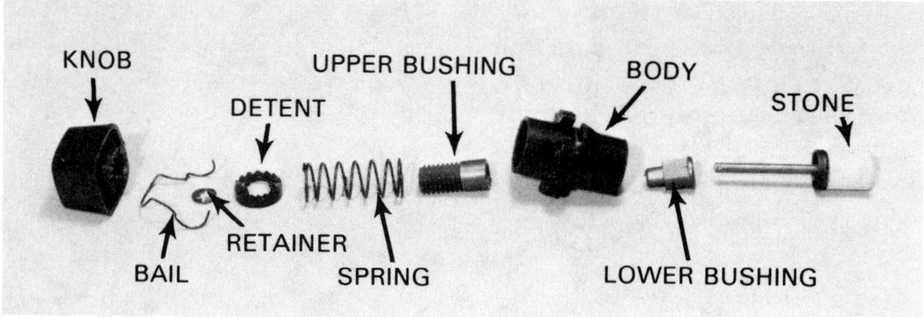

Fig. 9-17: Parts of a typical round stone automatic sharpener.

with each new chain installation. Under normal conditions, the average stone will average 25 to 30 touch-up sharpenings.

To replace the grinding stone, the typical automatic sharpening assembly must be removed. If the knob is not already separated from the assembly, rotate it clockwise until it does so (Fig. 9-18A). Remove the bail wire by snapping it up and over the sharpener body until it separates. Remove the sharpening body from the saw by turning it counterclockwise out of the bracket. Now, take a pair of pliers, "grab" the retaining washer, and squeeze. This buckles or breaks the retainer so that it can easily be removed (Fig. 9-18B). (Wear eye protection during this procedure.) The old grinding stone can now be taken out and discarded.

Before installing the new stone, make certain the upper and lower bushings are in place. Insert the new stone and place the spring in position (Fig. 9-18C).

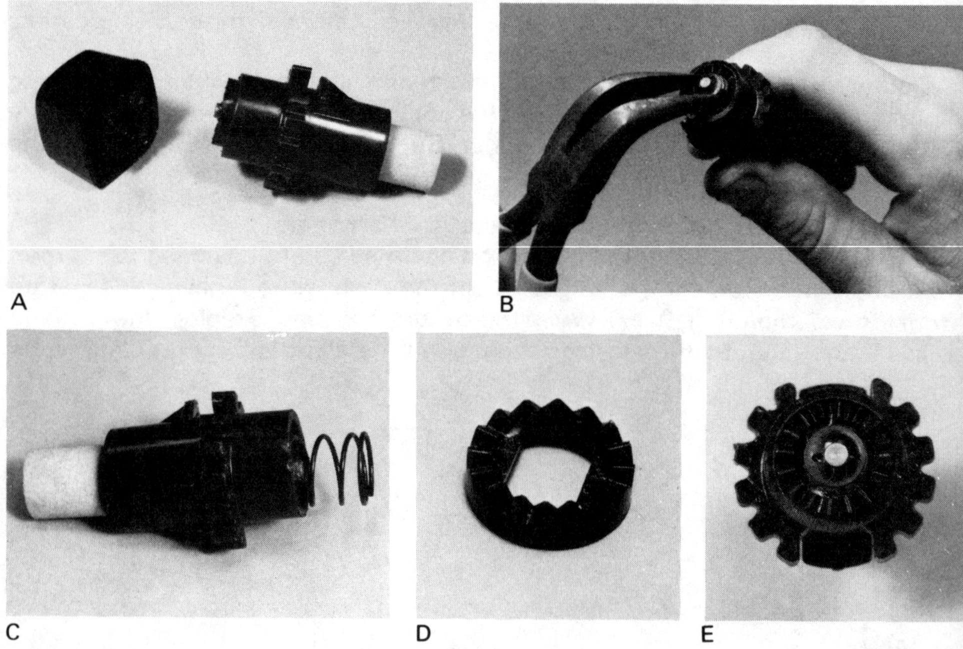

Fig. 9-18: Steps in replacing a round grinding stone in a typical automatic sharpener.

Install the detent with its teeth up onto the upper bushing (Fig. 9-18D). Make sure the detent matches the flats on the upper bushing. Then, compress the spring with the detent and push the new retaining washer supplied with the new stone onto the spindle until it bottoms out on the upper bushing (Fig. 9-18E).

The new grinding stone should now rotate freely, but have no upward and downward movement. The sharpening body can now be replaced on the saw, followed by the bail and adjustment knob. You can now adjust for subsequent sharpenings.

Chain Troubleshooting

Most chain problems are caused by three things: lack of lubrication, loose chain tension, and improper filing. Here are some of the more common signs to look for if your saw chain is not performing properly.

CUTTER TROUBLESHOOTING CHECKLIST

Trouble	Possible Cause	Remedy
Chain cuts very slowly. Severe damage on either side of top and/or side plates (Fig 9-19A).	Cutters striking materials other than wood.	File damaged area out of cutters. File both sides of cutter to same length. Reset depth gauges.
Chain cuts slowly. Light damage to cutting edges of top and/or side plates (Fig. 9-19B).	Cutters contacting light abrasive materials.	File damaged area out of cutters.
Chain dulls quickly. Feathered cutting edges on top plates (Fig. 9-19C).	File held too low when sharpening cutters.	Use proper filing method.
	File too small.	Sharpen with proper size file.
Chain will not cut properly and produces sawdust. Backslope on side plate cutting edges (Fig. 9-19D).	File held too high when sharpening cutters.	File cutters to recommended angle. Use proper filing method.
	File too large.	Sharpen with proper size file.
Chain dulls quickly. Hooks in cutting edges of side plates.	File held too low when sharpening cutters.	File cutters to recommended angles. Use proper filing method.
	File too small.	Sharpen with proper size file.
Slow-cutting. Blunt top plate cutting angle (Fig. 9-19E).	File held too high when sharpening cutters.	File cutters to recommended angle. Use proper filing method.
	File too large.	Sharpen with proper size file.
Chain is slow cutting. Top plate angles filed to less than the recommended degree (Fig. 9-19F).	File held at less than recommended angle.	File cutters to recommended angle. Use proper filing method.
Chain dulls rapidly. Top plate angles filed to greater than recommended degree (Fig. 9-19G).	File held at more than the recommended angle.	File to the recommended angle. Use proper filing method.

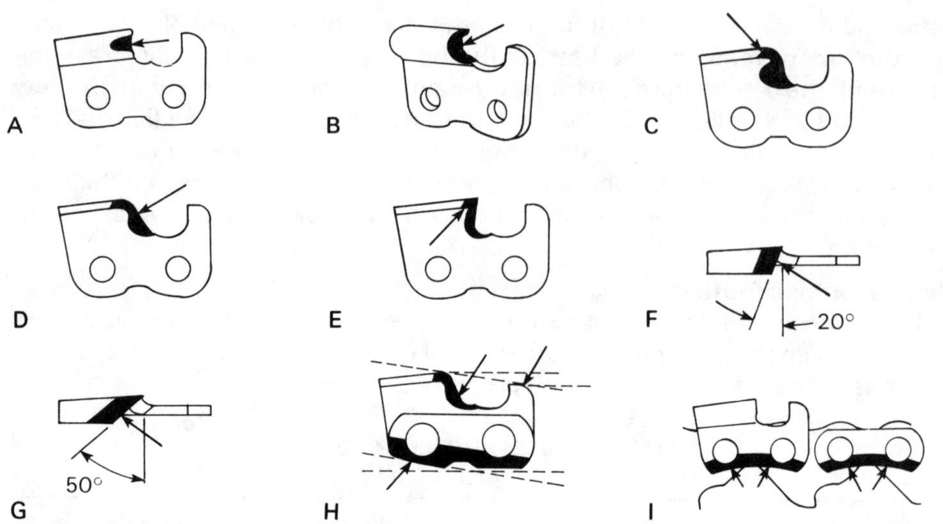

Fig. 9-19: Cutter tooth problems.

Trouble	Possible Cause	Remedy
Chain may kink. Excess heel wear on cutters and side straps (Fig. 9-19H).	Blunt top plate filing. Low depth gauges.	Use proper filing method. Keep cutters sharp.
	Forcing dull chain to cut. Forcing chain through frozen wood.	Never force chain to cut.
	Lack of lubrication.	Use sufficient lubrication.
Chain may kink. Concave wear on cutters and side strap bottom (Fig. 9-19I).	Tight chain tension on hard-nose bar.	Use sprocket-nose bar.
	Heavy undercutting or boring with hard-nose bar.	Reduced cutting with nose or top of bar.

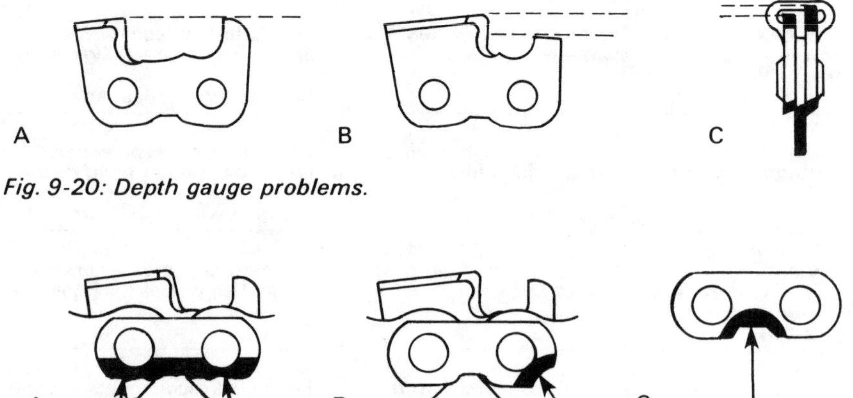

Fig. 9-20: Depth gauge problems.

Fig. 9-21: Tight joint problems.

DEPTH GAUGE TROUBLESHOOTING CHECKLIST

Trouble	Possible Cause	Remedy
Chain is slow cutting. High depth gauges (Fig. 9-20A).	Depth gauges never filed. Insufficient depth gauge filing.	Lower depth gauges to recommended setting.
Chain grabs, rough cutting. Low depth gauges (Fig. 9-20B).	Wrong depth gauge file guide setting used. No file guide used.	Have chain serviced. Replace chain when depth gauges are filed too low to be serviced.
Chain is rough cutting. Uneven depth gauge height (Fig. 9-20C).	Uneven depth gauge settings.	Use correct file guide setting. Keep all depth gauges at equal height. Repair guide bar.
Excessive bar wear is present. Peening on bottoms of cutters and side straps (Fig. 9-21A).	Loose chain tension.	Keep proper chain tension.
	Badly filed cutters. Forcing dull chain to cut.	Keep cutters sharp.
	Chain chatter.	Replace chains with severely tightened joints.
Chain kinks. Peening on front corners of cutters and side straps (Fig. 9-21B).	Loose chain tension.	Keep proper chain tension.
Chain kinks. Peened notches in side straps (Fig. 9-21C).	Worn spur sprocket.	Chain no longer serviceable, replace sprocket and chain.

DRIVE LINK TROUBLESHOOTING CHECKLIST

Trouble	Possible Cause	Remedy
Drive link bottoms worn straight (Fig. 9-22A).	Shallow bar groove in body of bar.	File top of drive link to clean bar groove.
		Replace bar.
Drive link bottoms worn in concave shape (Fig. 9-22B).	Shallow bar groove in nose of bar.	Replace bar.
	Worn tip.	Have bar nose rewelded.
Drive link bottoms battered or broken (Fig. 9-22C).	Chain jumping off revolving spur sprocket.	File burrs off drive links.
		Replace badly damaged links.
Drive link sides worn at bottom (Fig. 9-22D).	Drive links worn thin at bottoms.	Close groove in bar if possible.
		Replace bar.
		When problem persists, replace chain.
Peening on front and back of drive links (Fig. 9-22E).	Worn sprocket.	Replace sprocket.

Trouble	Possible Cause	Remedy
Various drive link wear patterns (Figs. 9-22F to 22J).	Worn bar groove—worn nose (Fig. 9-22F). Thin bar rails—nose area (Fig. 9-22G). Bar rails not flat (Fig. 9-22H). Wide and worn rails (Fig. 9-22I). Single rail worn down (Fig. 9-22J).	Have bar serviced. Replace bar.

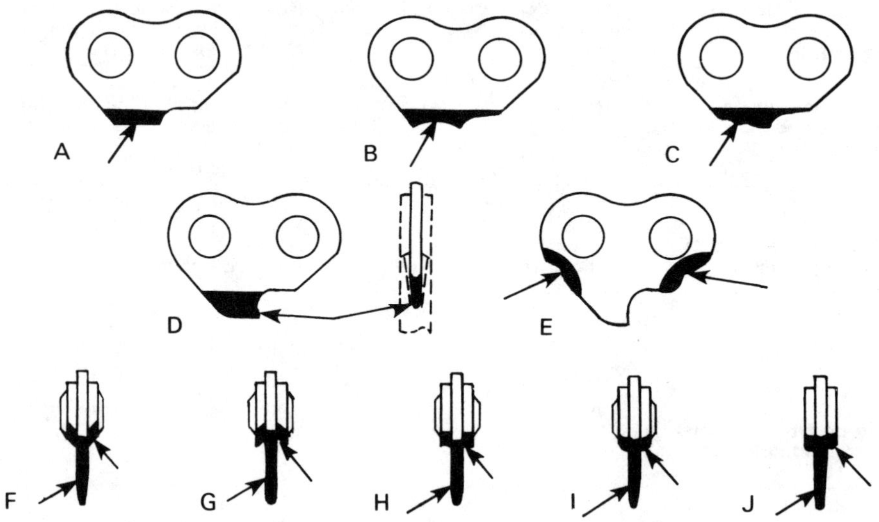

Fig. 9-22: Drive link problems.

Chain Repairs

If you strike a rock or hit a nail, even the best maintained saw chain is instantly in need of repair. A loose chain jumping the groove can cause damage to a dozen drive link tangs in a second. Because damaged drive tangs may cause deformation of the guide bar groove and rails or may damage the sprocket, chain repair is essential. Obtain the necessary spare parts from your dealer and keep the following points in mind before you rivet the new parts into place. For example, make sure that all cutters are set in the proper sequence and face in the right direction. Check to insure that the rivet holes of side links and cutters are countersunk on one side only. Be careful to place the countersunk side facing up.

When peening a rivet into place, be careful not to hit the side link with the hammer. If you bend it, a tight joint could result and tight joints can cause big problems. A chain with even one tight joint will most likely break, not at the tight link, but somewhere between the trouble spot and the sprocket. What is worse is that it will continue to break after each repair until the tight joint is found and replaced.

Watch also that you do not accidentally hammer a side link into an arc. This will result in the same problems caused by running a good chain on a worn sprocket—numerous burrs on the side links and cutter bottoms which grip the drive links and tighten the joints.

Removing Broken Drive Links. There are a number of inexpensive and simple-to-operate chain breakers available which make chain repair work faster and easier. You simply place the damaged section of the chain over one of the channels in the chain breaker and use the punch to knock out the rivet. Fit the chain into the smallest channel of the chain breaker so the cutter is on top (Fig. 9-23). If a drive link breaks at the rivet hole, place the chain on the chain breaker, hold the broken drive link together, and punch out the rivets. It is also possible to file or grind the rivet heads and then punch them out. Wear safety glasses when using the punch.

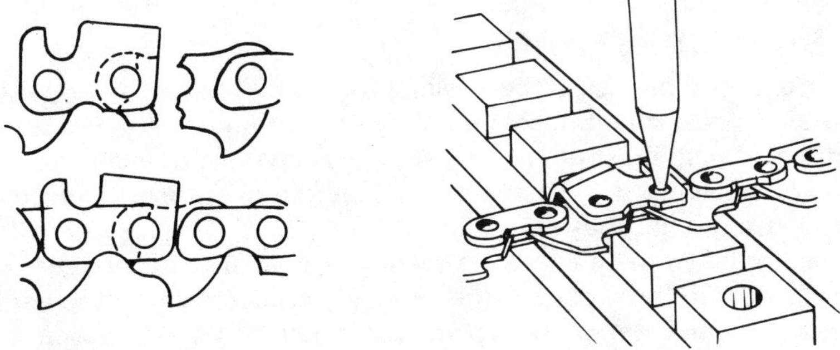

Fig. 9-23: Using a chain breaker to remove a broken drive link.

Putting New Parts on a Worn Chain. On a worn chain, the bottoms of the side straps and cutters will be worn down to some degree, and the bottoms of any new parts must be filed or ground to match (Fig. 9-24A). Otherwise, the new part or parts will ride higher than the rest of the chain, resulting in incorrect chain tension, drive link misalignment and breakage, and unnecessary bar and sprocket wear. If the new part is a cutter, its top plate and cutting edge will be higher than the rest of the cutters, causing excessive vibration and slow cutting. So be sure to file it to match the others.

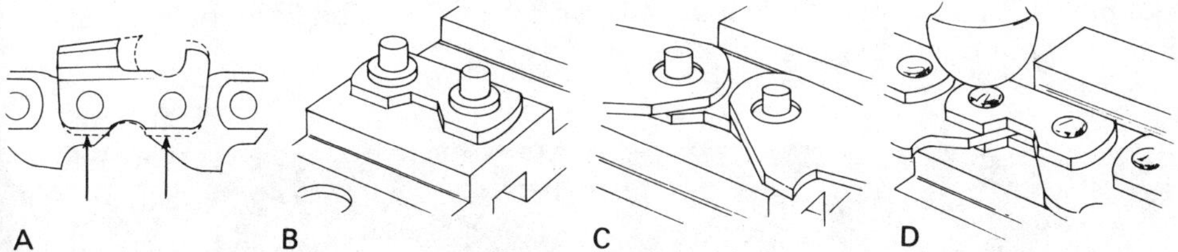

Fig. 9-24: Steps necessary to put a new part on a worn chain.

After filing, place the preset part on a flat surface (Fig. 9-24B) and install the chain on the new piece (Fig. 9-24C). Dimple on the tie straps, faces out. Then, carefully form the rivet heads with a hammer (Fig. 9-24D).

Where to Shorten or Lengthen a Chain. Most saw chains are joined with a tie strap between a right- and left-hand cutter. Some loops are joined between two left- or two right-hand cutters, and still others have two tie straps and a drive link between two cutters (Fig. 9-25). Thus, if the chain needs to be lengthened or shortened for any reason, these are the places to remove or add parts. Remem-

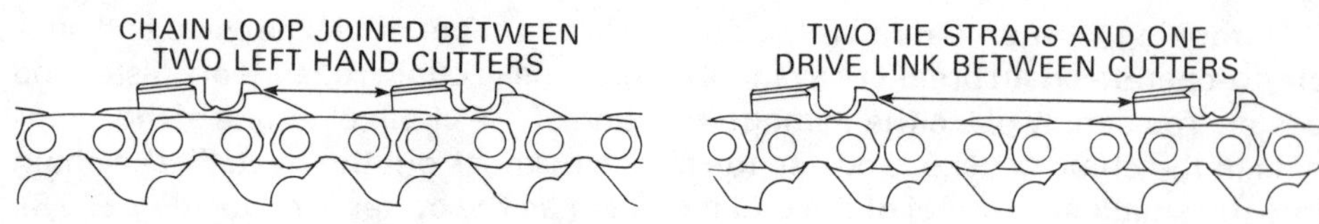

Fig. 9-25: Where to shorten or lengthen a chain.

ber when removing links to obtain correct chain tension, never remove more than three links from the chain. Removal of more than three links could result in improper pitch.

GUIDE BAR MAINTENANCE

Most guide bar problems can be avoided for a long time by merely keeping a well-maintained saw chain. Incorrect filing and nonuniform cutter and depth gauge settings cause most guide bar problems—mainly, uneven bar wear. As the bar wears unevenly, it widens, and chain clatter, rivet popping, and difficulty in making a straight cut may result.

Even if you pride yourself on taking extraordinary care of your saw chain, do not dismiss bar maintenance as unnecessary. Periodically turn the bar upside down to ensure even wear on the top and bottom of the bar. If you work one side down too far before turning the bar over, all-around wear is accelerated.

The guide groove should be cleaned every time the chain is removed. Run a depth gauge tang or similarly sized instrument along the groove until all residue is cleared (Fig. 9-26). Clogged grooves tend to bind the center link tangs of the chain. Also, keep both sides of the groove at the point of chain entry properly "funneled" to avoid damage to the drive link tangs.

Oil passages at the base of the guide bar should be cleaned periodically to ensure proper lubrication of the chain and bar groove. This can be done with the depth gauge tang or any instrument small enough to insert into the passages (Fig. 9-27). The condition of the oil passages should be checked before each use of the saw. While running the saw, press the manual oiler button a few times. If the passages are clear, the chain will give off a spray of oil from the nose of the bar with a momentary acceleration of the throttle.

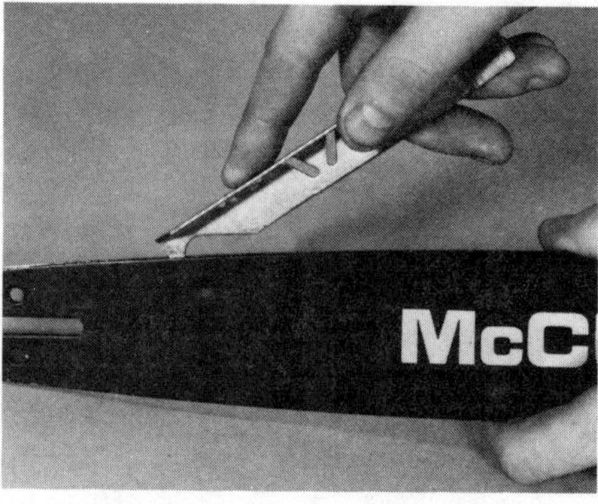

Fig. 9-26: Cleaning the guide groove.

Fig. 9-27: Cleaning the oil passages.

Oiler Adjustment and Maintenance. As mentioned in earlier chapters, some chain saws are equipped with a manual oiler, either as the sole means of lubrication or as a back-up system to the automatic oiler. To check the manual oiler, depress the manual oiler button two or three times. Oil should appear on the top of the bar near the engine. If it does not, the oiling slots and grooves should be cleaned as described above. When your machine is equipped with both automatic and manual systems, supplement the oil supply to the chain by pressing the manual oiler button frequently.

The automatic oiler is adjusted at the factory for average cutting conditions. Oil flow may be adjusted, however, for special conditions or individual requirements. With most saws, turn the adjustment screw clockwise to reduce oil flow and counterclockwise to increase it (Fig. 9-28). However, the adjustment screw should not be turned more than one quarter of a turn at one time. Check the oil flow after each adjustment. When more oil is needed for short periods of time, it is wiser to use the manual oiler as a supplement and make no adjustment to the automatic oiler screw.

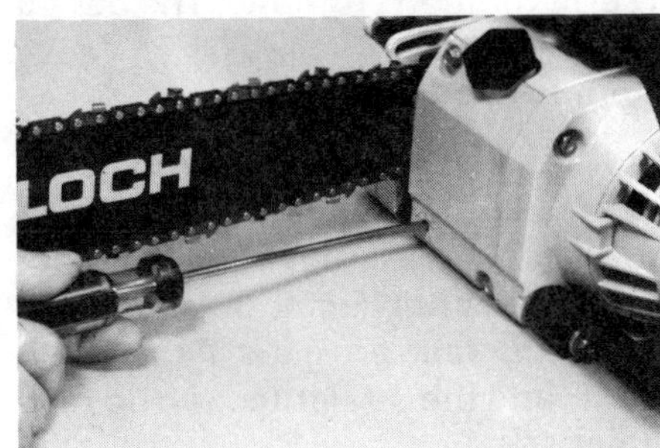

Fig. 9-28: Adjusting a typical automatic oiler.

If the chain becomes dry or the bar becomes hot when the saw is in operation, it is a good indicator that one or a combination of three things may be happening. The oil reservoir may be empty, the automatic or manual oiler may be faulty, or the oil slot might be plugged with grime, dirt, or wood chips. If cleaning the oil holes, filling the oil reservoir, or adjusting the oil flow does not solve the problem, maintenance to the oil pump may be required. Service by an authorized service dealer, as stated previously, is the only solution in this case.

Lubrication of Sprocket-Tip. Normal sprocket-tip bars require lubrication. However, more lubrication is always necessary for professional usage and under the following circumstances.

1. Continuous cutting of dry or highly abrasive wood.
2. Continuous boring cuts.
3. Continuous cutting with the bar tip.
4. Continuous cutting in wet or snowy conditions.

Under these circumstances, lubrication is recommended after every hour of hard usage or after three tanks of gas are consumed. It is very important to thoroughly clean the bar tip before lubrication.

Three methods of lubrication for the sprocket-tip may be employed:

1. **Needle nose-grease gun.** Clean out the grease hole. Then, insert the nozzle of the grease gun in the grease hole (Fig. 9-29A) and pump until the grease

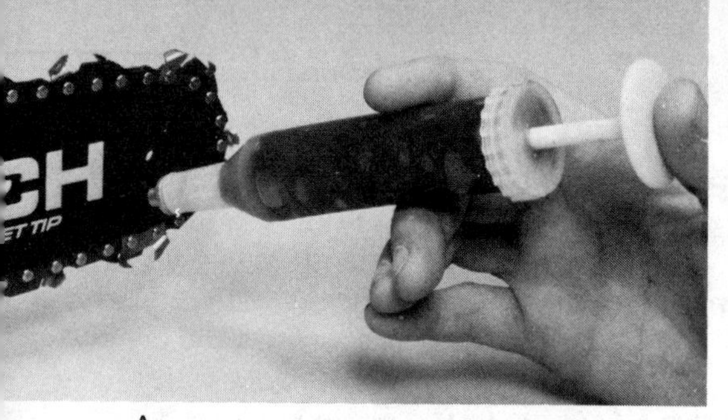

A

B

Fig. 9-29: Two methods of lubricating the sprocket-tip.

comes out from around the sprocket. Rotate the nose sprocket while pumping the grease into the bearings. Repeat on the other side of the bar. Use a good quality lithium-based bearing grease.

2. **Oil can.** Squirt the appropriate weight motor oil (SAE 10 in cold weather, SAE 30 in hot weather) into the lubrication hole while turning the sprocket. Repeat on the other side of the bar.

3. **Oil soak.** Fill a small container with clean oil and submerge the bar tip in the oil (Fig. 9-29B). Rotate the sprocket several revolutions by hand. The bar tip may be submerged overnight for maximum lubrication.

Guide Bar Troubles

The guide bars on even the best kept saws wear, and you should periodically check the bar rails to see that they are square and flat. To do this, simply set the rails on a flat surface or use a square. Also, check for inside groove wear by placing a straightedge against the side of the bar and one cutter (Fig. 9-30). If there is clearance between the bar and the straightedge, the rails are good. If the chain leans and there is no clearance between the bar and the straightedge, the rails are worn and the guide bar needs replacement.

Typical guide bar problems, their causes, and remedies are given in the following chart.

GUIDE BAR TROUBLESHOOTING CHECKLIST

Trouble	Possible Cause	Remedy
Worn bar rails (Fig. 9-31A).	Normal bar wear after extended period of time.	Replace bar.
Thin low rails on one or both sides of bar (Fig. 9-31B).	Chain lean to one side. Extensive crooked cutting. Forcing a dull chain to cut. Damage to cutters on one side of chain.	Replace bar. Sharpen chain correctly.
Blue friction spots on rail (Fig. 9-31C).	Rail pinches partially closed, resulting in drive link friction.	Replace bar.
Sections broken out of the hard-tip nose (Fig. 9-31D) or split nose area on sprocket tip bar (Fig. 9-31E).	Drive links forced sideways during saw operation. Repeated pinching of bar during saw operation.	Replace bar.
Nose rail split at bottom of groove. Bar possibly bent in nose area or along entire length (Fig. 9-31F).	Operating accident. Excessive side pressure exerted on nose rail.	Replace bar.

Trouble	Possible Cause	Remedy
Chipped rail (Fig. 9-31G).	Continuous pressure on bar in one area. Dull chain. Loose chain tension.	Reverse bar to reduce wear. Replace bar. (To avoid damage to new bar, tension and sharpen chain.)

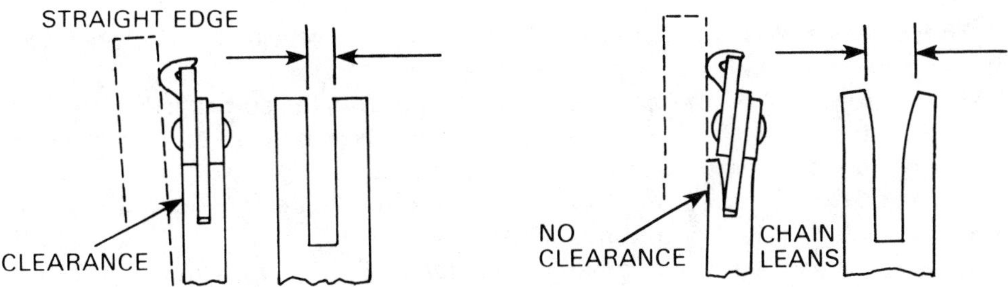

Fig. 9-30: How to determine guide bar replacement.

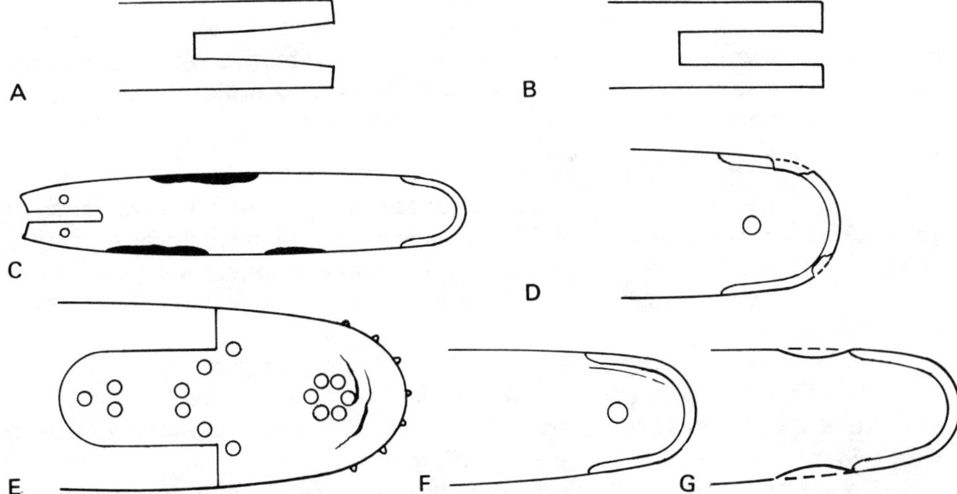

Fig. 9-31: Guide bar problems.

SPROCKET-TIP NOSE BAR TROUBLESHOOTING CHECKLIST

Trouble	Possible Cause	Remedy
Nose area blue in one or two spots or along entire bar (Fig. 9-32A).	Pinched nose, resulting in increased sprocket friction.	Problem in nose bearing area: replace bar. Bars with replaceable sprocket-nose: replace sprocket-nose. Laminated bars: replace bar.
Chipping at nose connection on bars with replaceable noses (Fig. 9-32B).	Continuous pressure in connection area. Heavy limbing at connection point.	Replace nose assembly, dress rail bar and nose to match.

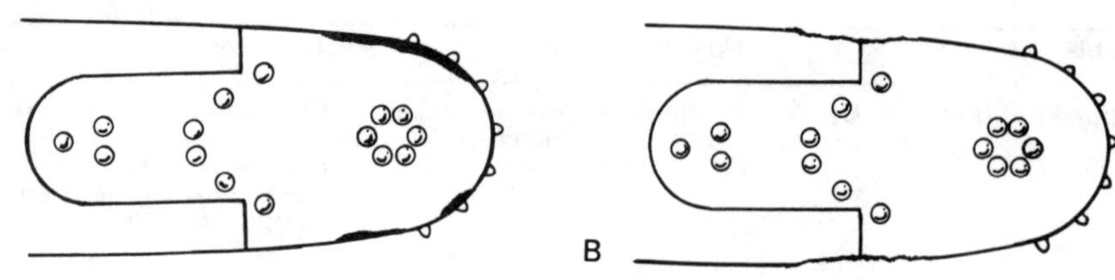

Fig. 9-32: Sprocket-tip nose problems.

To Replace a Nose Sprocket Tip. If a typical nose sprocket tip needs replacement, proceed as follows:

1. Carefully drill off the heads of the rivets holding the sprocket (Fig. 9-33A).
2. Punch out the rivets (Fig. 9-33B) and clean the nose area of the bar. Then, remove the old sprocket tip assembly (Fig. 9-33C).
3. Insert the new sprocket tip assembly into the guide bar (Fig. 9-33D) until the rivet holes in the bar and nose assembly line up.
4. Insert the new rivets and peen them gently (Fig. 9-33E). Do not hit the bar body.
5. Insert the nozzle of the grease gun in the grease hole (Fig. 9-33F) and pump until the grease comes out of the nose tip.

If the nose rails are spread open after removing the old sprocket tip, they may be closed by inserting the old inner race in its approximate position. Clamp the guide bar in a vise over the rivet area. Then, hammer the rail closed with a plastic or rawhide hammer. Never use a steel hammer.

DRIVE SPROCKET CARE

A worn drive sprocket will damage and weaken a saw chain beyond repair. If your sprocket looks worn (Fig. 9-34), replace it immediately. Never try to file, straighten, or weld a bad sprocket. Remember that a chain costs approximately four times as much as a sprocket, so there is no economy in using a worn sprocket with a new chain.

To avoid sprocket problems, keep the following points in mind:

1. Check the sprocket when you install a new chain. Replace if worn.
2. Keep the chain properly tensioned. Check the tensioning instructions in your owner's manual or those given in Chapter 2.
3. Grease the bearing whenever the sprocket is removed from the saw.
4. Keep the chain cutters correctly sharpened.
5. Use plenty of oil when cutting.
6. Keep the guide bar rails in good condition.

Sprocket Replacement. While there are various styles of sprockets used with chain saws, the replacement procedure of a typical sprocket is as follows:

1. Remove the chain brake assembly, bar and chain, and the starter housing. Disconnect the spark plug wire and remove the plug.
2. Lock the crankshaft in the manner prescribed by the manufacturer (Fig. 9-35A).
3. Turn the clutch nut *clockwise* (generally a left-hand thread) to remove it (Fig. 9-35B), then remove the dust plate and clutch.
4. Remove the sprocket and drum assembly. Lubricate the bearing with a good grade of non-fibrous chassis grease whenever replacing the sprocket and

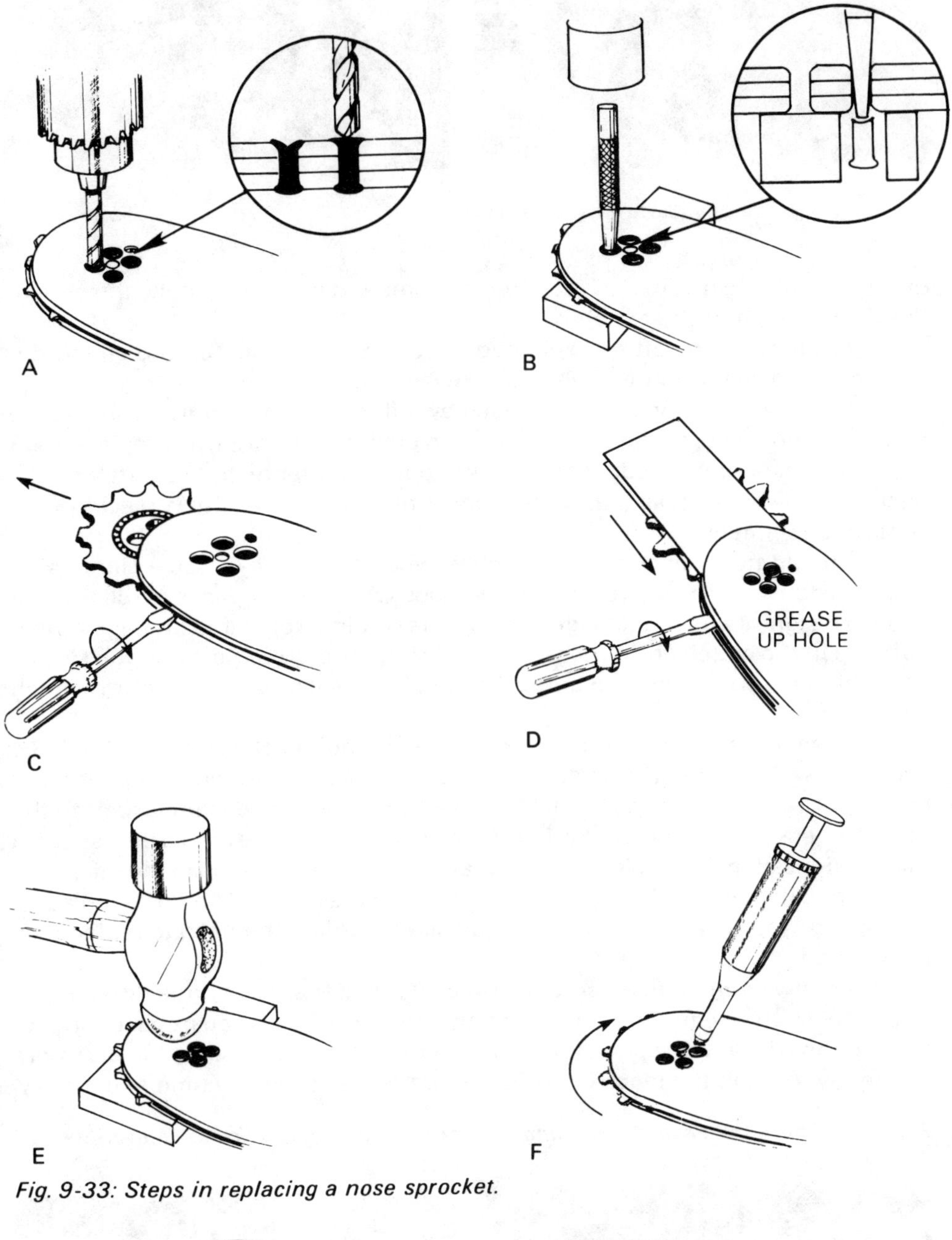

A

B

C

GREASE
UP HOLE

D

E

F

Fig. 9-33: Steps in replacing a nose sprocket.

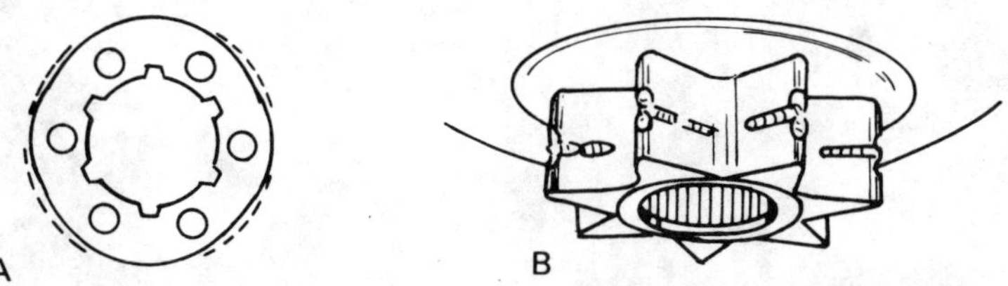

Fig. 9-34: Drive sprocket problems: (A) worn rim sprocket and (B) worn spur.

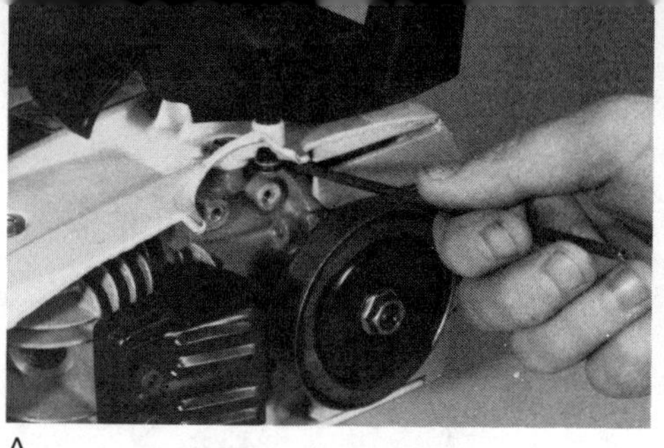
A

B

Fig. 9-35: Replacing a worn drive sprocket.

drum assembly. Now, install the new sprocket and drum assembly, the clutch, the dust plate, and the clutch nut.

5. Lock the crankshaft as explained in step two, and tighten the clutch nut securely by turning it in a *counterclockwise* direction.

Variations exist in the sprockets used by different manufacturers, so be sure to use the model number of your saw when buying or ordering any replacement sprockets. If there is any doubt at all, ask your dealer for help. Mismatching the pitches between sprockets and saw chains has ruined many new pieces of expensive equipment.

You should never operate a chain saw when there is excessive clutch slippage. A chain that moves very slowly or stops when the engine is at full throttle is a sure sign of clutch slippage. This will result in a rapid and damaging heat build-up in the clutch and clutch drum. This is a serious problem and you should have the saw serviced by your authorized dealer as soon as you detect any clutch slippage.

If your saw is equipped with a chain brake, it and the clutch drum should be kept as clean and free of sawdust as possible to allow free movement and full contact of the brake band. The thickness of the brake band is important to the effectiveness of the chain brake. For this reason, it should be regularly inspected for any signs of measurable wear or for any noticeable variation in the thickness of the band (Fig. 9-36). If such wear is noted, the brake band should be replaced. Check with your chain saw dealer for advice regarding the need to replace the brake band.

Proper saw chain, guide bar, and sprocket maintenance is not a difficult job, but it is a job that requires some time and effort. Any hours you put in caring for these parts will be well spent. Well-conditioned saws cut faster, safer, and more efficiently. And, in the long run, that is what really saves you time and money.

Fig. 9-36: Check the chain brake band for uneven wear. If it indicates uneven wear, it must be replaced.

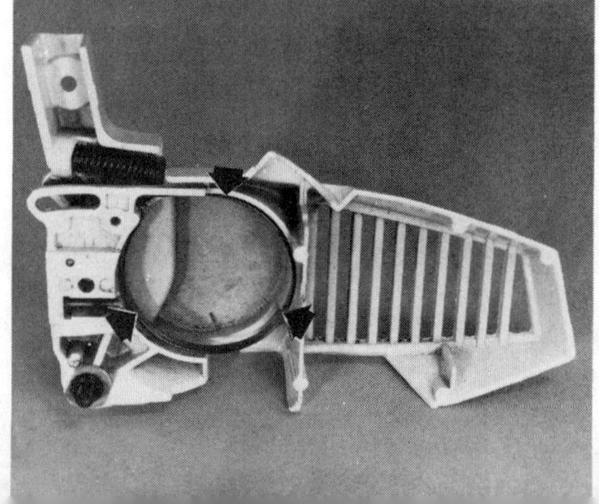

Engine Maintenance and Repair 10

A chain saw with cutters oiled and filed to perfection, a woodcutter brimming with enthusiasm, and a stubborn engine that refuses to start or run efficiently add up to a frustrating and nonproductive day's work. A good engine maintenance program of regular inspection and care will help avoid such disasters and increase the life span and performance levels of your chain saw.

FUEL AND INDUCTION SYSTEM

Because the crankcase of the two-cycle engine acts as a transfer pump for the air-fuel mixture, lubrication of the engine depends on the addition of oil to the gasoline. When the mixture passes through the carburetor, the gasoline becomes highly vaporized by the stream of air, while the oil is broken into tiny droplets which lubricate all the surfaces with which they come in contact. Some oil remains in the crankcase, but the greater quantity passes through the combustion chamber, where it is burned, and out the exhaust port.

As described in Chapter 2, the correct quantity, grade, and type of oil, as well as thorough mixing of gasoline and oil before using, are very important. The quantity of oil to be mixed with gasoline will vary from engine manufacturer to engine manufacturer as will the grade of oil. But the manufacturers' recommendations should always be followed since they know the lubrication requirements of their engines best. Several manufacturers market two-cycle engine oils and concentrated oils blended especially for use with their chain saws. These should be used whenever available, although any high grade two-cycle oil will do. Never use a multi-viscosity detergent motor oil intended for four-cycle engines because it will leave harmful deposits within the engine.

The grade of gasoline used in preparing this fuel mixture is equally important. Never use a high lead content (premium), no-lead, or low lead gasoline in any two-cycle engine. Uncontaminated, regular grade gasoline (around 88 octane) works best in chain saw engines. The proper gasoline to oil mixture varies slightly depending on the saw's manufacturer. Check your owner's manual to be sure you have the correct mix or check page 18 for complete information.

Fuel Filter

The fuel tank filter prevents dirt from entering the fuel line to the carburetor. After a while, dirt will build up on the filter and will cut down the flow of fuel. Or, if water is permitted to enter the fuel tank, the water will get into the filter and prevent the flow of fuel to the carburetor. If any condition affects the filter, install a new filter.

To change a filter for most saws, reach into the fuel tank with a hooked wire and carefully draw out the fuel pick-up line which connects to the carburetor. Be

Fig. 10-1: Steps in cleaning an air filter.

careful not to disconnect this hose from the carburetor. Pull out the old filter from the hose end and replace it. Check the fuel line for kinks and split or loose fitting ends. Replace the line if necessary. When placing the filter back into the tank, make sure that it reaches to the bottom. If this is not so, the engine will not be able to utilize all the fuel in the tank. Never operate the chain saw without a fuel filter. If you cannot find a hose, the pick-up line is elsewhere in the tank and must be replaced by your service dealer.

Fuel Cap

The fuel tank cap of most chain saws is vented to prevent buildup of either pressure or vacuum in the tank. Both conditions will affect operation of the engine. The vent can become plugged through the use of dirty fuel or dirt falling into the fuel tank during refueling operations. (On some small saws, the vent is located in the fuel tank.) If pressure or vacuum develops, have your authorized service dealer check the unit.

Air Filters

Never operate a chain saw without an air filter; damaging dust or dirt will be sucked into the engine if you do. A clean air filter is essential for the efficient operation of an engine. It should be cleaned daily or even more often, depending on the cutting conditions. To clean a typical air filter, close the carburetor choke to prevent particles from entering the cylinder and remove the air filter cover by loosening its screw (Fig. 10-1A). Then, lift off the air filter (Fig. 10-1B). Wearing eye protection, blow the filter clean with low air pressure (Fig. 10-1C), or wash it in clean kerosene (Fig. 10-1D) or other solvent recommended by the saw's manufacturer. (Never use fuel as solvent.) Dry the filter in the open air, well away from any open flame.

Before replacing the clean air filter, remove any sawdust or dirt which may have collected in the filter housing. Reinstall the air filter and cover, making sure the top edge of the cover fits into the retaining ridge on the air box cover.

The air filter should be replaced after several washings. When cutting under extremely dusty conditions, carry a number of clean filters and change the filter as needed during the day's work.

Starter Cover and Cooling Fins

The air inlet openings of the starter cover and the cylinder cooling fins must be kept clean to help prevent overheating of the engine. To clean these air inlet openings of a typical saw, remove the starter cover and use a small wooden scraper to remove the packed dirt and sawdust from the openings (Fig. 10-2A). Finish cleaning the cover with a soft bristle brush. Make sure the starter pulley turns freely and easily.

Scrape all the grass, wood chips, dirt, and other debris from the cooling fins on the cylinder head with a stiff brush or thin scraper (Fig. 10-2B). (If the saw is equipped with a chain brake, it must be removed before cleaning the fins.) Clean the vanes on the flywheel and the other parts of the engine that became visible when the starter cover was removed. When reinstalling the starter cover, pull the starter rope slowly so the starter can engage the flywheel properly. With some saws, when reinstalling the starter cover, ensure that the starter pawls are aligned at the top and bottom of the saw. Slide the cover into position lining up the screw holes and making sure that the retaining guide overlaps the housing at the front of the saw (Fig. 10-2C).

Carburetor Adjustments

Rough running or idling, frequent stalling, or chain rotation while the saw is at idle are all signs that the carburetor is in need of attention. All adjustments should be made with extreme caution. It is very easy to over-adjust and cause damage to the carburetor. Always use a properly fitting screwdriver, and be sure the fuel cap is breathing properly and the air filter is clean before making any adjustments. Follow the procedures described in the owner's manual for your saw or the general instructions given in Chapter 2.

Spark Plug

Incorrect engine oil or fuel mixture, bad carburetor adjustments, or excessive engine flooding during starting will all cause deposits to form on the spark plug electrodes. Even if these problems are not present, cleaning the electrodes will be necessary after many hours of operation. A clean, correctly gapped plug assures the finest engine performance.

Set the ignition switch on the OFF position. Then, disconnect the black rubber connector on the end of the wire from the spark plug by twisting and pulling it at the same time (Fig. 10-3A). Always remove the spark plug with the properly sized spark plug wrench (Fig. 10-3B); never use any other tool. Clean the electrodes with emery cloth (Fig. 10-3C) and/or a sharp knife, and blow all the dust away from the electrode (Fig. 10-3D). Wear eye protection during this procedure. Do not use a grit-type cleaning tool to clean the electrodes.

The electrode air gap should be set at 0.025 inches (0.635 mm) on most chain saws (Fig. 10-4). Check your owner's manual to be precise. Always bend the side electrode toward the center electrode when setting the gap. Rounded or pit-

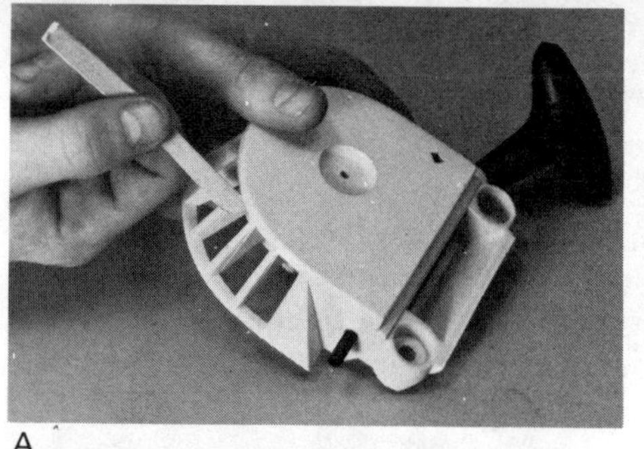
A

B

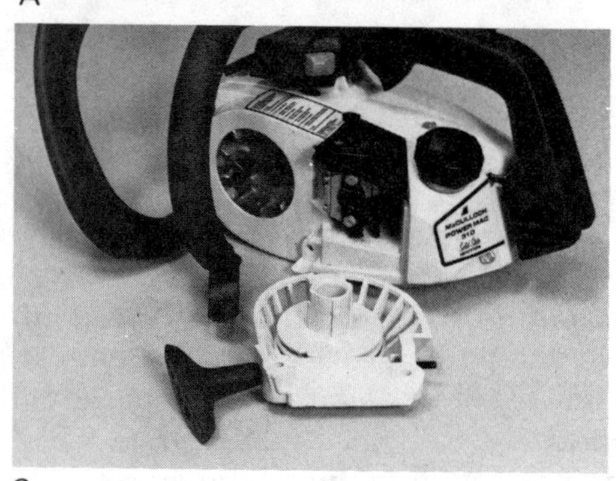
C

Fig. 10-2: Cleaning the starter cover and cooling fins.

A

B

C

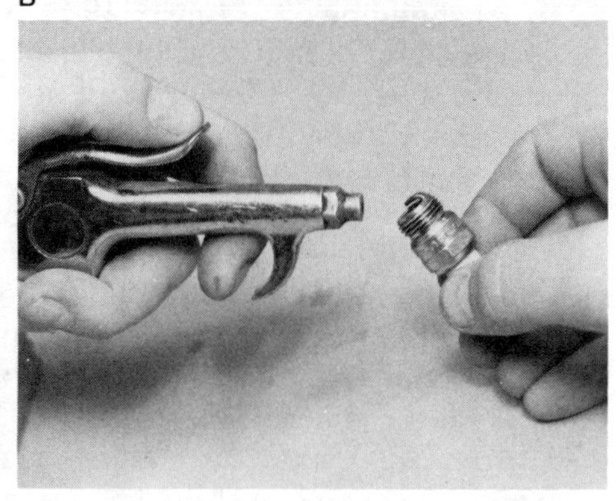
D

Fig. 10-3: Steps in cleaning a spark plug.

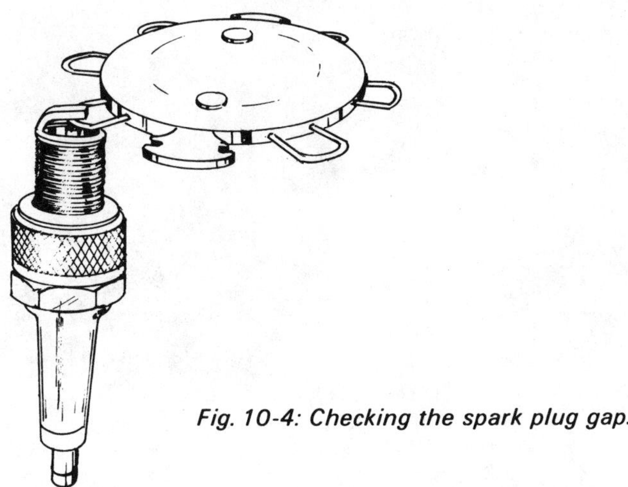

Fig. 10-4: Checking the spark plug gap.

ted electrodes should be filed smooth and square to induce the spark to jump the gap.

The condition of the spark plug is a good indicator of how your engine is running (Fig. 10-5). After considerable service, the plug should be dry and black or light gray to tan in appearance. Sooty, black carbon on the plug's bottom or electrodes indicates that the engine has been getting too much fuel, or too much oil may be in the fuel mix. The ignition voltage might also be too low, or the wrong heat range plug is being used. If the engine is running too hot, or there is an air leak in the fuel system or engine seals, the plugs will have white to light gray powder deposits. It may also have a burnt, gray, blistered look on the electrode's porcelain insulator. The center electrode may also appear melted and the insulator burned. Additives in the oil or gasoline that is used in the fuel mix or the improper mix ratio may cause yellow ash deposits to form on the plug. Core bridging or gap bridging with carbon or other materials is another sign of this problem.

While the spark plug is out, the ignition system should be tested to see whether or not there is a good spark being generated by the magneto. To do this, insert a 1/4 inch (.6 cm) diameter metal rod (a screw works nicely) into the spark plug boot to contact the spring connector inside. Holding the spark plug boot well back on the insulation, position the rod so there will be an air gap of 1/4 inch (.6 cm) between the rod and a good ground (metal) *away* from the spark plug hole (Fig. 10-6). With the ignition switch turned to the ON position, crank the engine briskly and observe whether or not a spark jumps the 1/4 inch (.6 cm) gap. In bright sunlight, the snap of a strong spark can be heard even though it cannot be seen.

A broad blue or white spark indicates that the magneto is operating properly. If this is the case, reinstall the clean and re-gapped spark plug and the rubber spark plug wire assembly. If there is no spark generated *at all*, have the ignition system checked by your service dealer.

Muffler, Exhaust Port, and Spark Arrestor-Screen Maintenance

Operating a chain saw with a dirty or faulty muffler can lead to damage to the

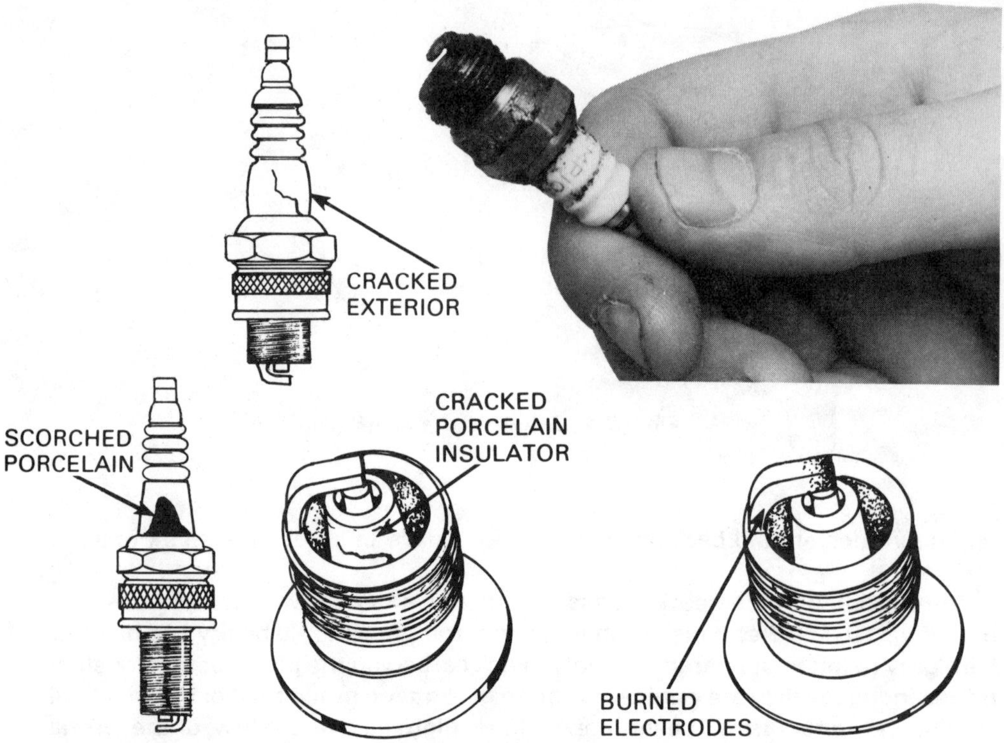

Fig. 10-5: A visual check of your spark plug can often help to determine engine troubles.

Fig. 10-6: To check the spark, be sure that you have a good ground away from the spark plug hole since any residue fuel in that hole could be ignited by the spark.

engine; therefore, it is advisable to remove, clean, and inspect the muffler periodically. One thing you should never do is operate the engine without a muffler. Check the muffler and exhaust port for carbon buildup and be sure that your saw is equipped with a spark arrestor screen that is in good condition. These screens are required when working in any National Forest as well as most state and public woodlands (check for any specific local regulations).

Spark arrestors are designed by the manufacturer to comply with all forestry regulations. They must, however, be cleaned daily with a bristle brush. If a spark arrestor becomes damaged in any way, it should be replaced. The exhaust ports should be cleaned monthly or after 25 hours of operation.

When servicing the exhaust system, remove the chain brake (if the saw is so equipped), and unscrew the screws which hold the exhaust deflector onto the muffler. Then, remove the remaining screws and separate the muffler from the cylinder (Fig. 10-7A). Clean away all carbon deposits with a scraper blade, wire brush, or by washing them with a clean solvent (Fig. 10-7B). Be careful not to damage the exhaust chamber or screen. While the muffler is removed from the saw, examine the exhaust port for evidence of carbon around the port. Clean the port in the following manner.

1. Take out the spark plug and pull the starter rope slowly until the piston covers the exhaust port completely.
2. Clean in and around the port with a wooden scraper. Do not use any metal or sharp-edged tool that might slip and scratch the piston or rings.
3. After cleaning, turn the saw exhaust-side down and blow or shake away any loose particles. Wear eye protection while doing this.
4. Crank the engine several times to blow out the remaining particles. Replace the spark plug and be sure that the spark arrestor screen is properly fitted into place.

A

B

Fig. 10-7: Cleaning the muffler and exhaust port.

Engine Troubleshooting Checklist

In spite of how well a chain saw is maintained, problems do come along. The following trouble guide will help solve the more common engine problems:

ENGINE TROUBLESHOOTING CHECKLIST

Trouble	Possible Cause	Remedy
Engine will not start.	Fuel filter clogged or frosted over.	Clean filter (temporary) and replace when possible.
	Breaker points out of adjustment or dirty.	Clean, readjust or replace points as needed.*
	In extreme temperatures, fuel lines or carburetor icing.	Remove lines and clean. Add de-ice additive to fuel (follow owner's manual recommendations).
	Bad condenser.	Replace condenser.*
	Faulty magneto or coil.	Replace magneto or coil.*
	Electronic ignition faulty.	Replace unit.*
	Faulty ignition components.	Repair or replace.
	Carburetor malfunctions (plugged jet, impulse hole, etc.).	Repair carburetor as needed.*
Engine dies.	Improper carburetor adjustments.	Readjust carburetor.
	Dirty or burned points.	Clean or replace points.*
	Water, ice or dirt in fuel.	Clean or replace fuel filter, drain tank.
	Fuel intake line kinked or partially plugged.	Clean or untwist line, replace, if necessary.
	Ignition wires short-circuiting or grounding.	Check all wire and connections and repair or replace.*
	Seal(s) leak.	Replace seals.*
	Defective coil.	Replace coil and condenser.*
	Faulty electronic ignition.	Replace unit.*
Engine will not accelerate.	Low-speed mixture screw set too lean.	Adjust carburetor.
	Chain too tight.	Readjust chain tension.
	Carburetor defects or blockage.	Repair carburetor.*
	Throttle linkage bent.	Straighten linkage.
	Point setting off.	Reset points.*
Chain continues moving with throttle released.	Improper carburetor adjustment.	Readjust carburetor.
	Sprocket bearing worn out or dry.	Replace bearing.*
	Broken or weak clutch springs.	Replace springs.*
Erratic idling with little or no response to carburetor adjustments.	Loose carburetor.	Tighten carburetor.
	Fuel line stretched, damaged or loose.	Replace fuel line.*
	Defective spacer.	Replace carburetor spacer.*
	Split fuel pick-up line.	Replace line.*

ENGINE TROUBLESHOOTING CHECKLIST

Trouble	Possible Cause	Remedy
Erratic idling with little or no response to carburetor adjustments.	Air leak due to worn or damaged main bearing seal or crankcase cover gasket.	Replace seals or gasket.*
	Fuel line fitting loose.	Tighten fitting.
	Air leak due to carburetor gasket.	Replace gasket.*
	Breaker points set too wide.	Readjust points.*
	Cracked casting.	Replace casting.*
	Wrong type of gas being used.	Drain tank and fill with correct fuel mixture.
	Condenser defective.	Replace condenser.*
	Coil windings broken.	Replace coil.*
	Loose wire.	Repair.*
Engine will not idle.	Incorrect adjustment of idle fuel and/or speed screws.	Adjust screw(s).
	Condenser defective.	Replace condenser.*
	Coil windings broken or intermittent.	Replace coil.*
	Loose wire in ignition system.	Repair.*
	Idle discharge or air mixture ports clogged.	Clean ports.
	Fuel passage clogged.	Clean passage.
	Welch plug covering idle ports not sealing properly.	Replace plug.
	Throttle shutter misaligned.	Align shutter.
Engine runs rich.	Leaky inlet needle.	Clean or replace.*
	Carburetor adjusted improperly.	Readjust carburetor.
	Inlet lever adjusted too high.	Readjust carburetor.
Engine runs lean.	Fuel tank vent or cap plugged.	Clean vent or cap.
	Leak in fuel line fittings between tank and carburetor.	Tighten or replace as necessary.*
	Filter in carburetor or filter in fuel pick-up plugged.	Clean carburetor screen, clean or fuel pick-up filter.
	Fuel orifice plugged.	Clean orifice.
	Hole in fuel metering diaphragm or fuel pump diaphragm.	Replace diaphragm.*
	Metering lever not set properly.	Adjust lever.
	Cracked crankcase.	Replace crankcase.*
	Crankcase air leak.	Repair or replace.*
Loss of power.	Dull chain.	Sharpen chain.
	Improper chain tension.	Adjust tension.
	Chain not oiling.	Clean oil port.
	Clogged air filter.	Clean air filter.
	Dirty muffler and/or exhaust ports.	Clean muffler and/or exhaust ports.

ENGINE TROUBLESHOOTING CHECKLIST

Trouble	Possible Cause	Remedy
Loss of power.	High speed mixture screw improperly set.	Adjust high speed mixture screw.
	Dirty carburetor.	Clean carburetor.
	Spark arrestor screen clogged.	Clean spark arrestor screen.
	Points improperly set.	Adjust points.
	Dirty fuel filter.	Clean filter.
	Oil breaking down.	Use proper oil.
	Oil tank check valve leaking into cylinder or crankcase.	Replace check valve.*
Engine overheats.	Cylinder fins clogged.	Clean fins.
	Exhaust ports and/or muffler plugged.	Clean exhaust ports and/or muffler.
	High-speed adjustment too lean.	Adjust high-speed screw.
	No oil in gasoline.	Empty tank and refill with correct mixture.
	Oil breaking down.	Use proper oil.
	Points set too wide (early ignition).	Adjust points.*
	Unleaded fuel being used.	Use correct fuel.
Restart difficult when saw is hot.	Carburetor fuel inlet needle leaking.	Adjust inlet lever or replace inlet needle.*
	Vapor lock.	See owner's manual for hot saw starting techniques.
Heavy smoke, low power.	Oil tank check valve leaking oil into cylinder or crankcase.	Replace check valve.*

*Recommended for servicing by an authorized service dealer.

Fig. 10-8: Keeping the chain saw well maintained and using the proper cutting procedures will lead to trouble-free chain saw use.

PREVENTIVE MAINTENANCE

A good preventive maintenance program of regular inspection and care will increase life and improve performance of your chain saw (Fig. 10-8). This maintenance check chart is a guide for such a program. Cleaning, adjustment, and parts replacement may, under certain conditions, be required at more frequent intervals than those indicated.

PREVENTIVE MAINTENANCE CHECK CHART

ITEM	MAINTENANCE	FREQUENCY			
		Daily	Weekly	Monthly	As Req'd
Screws, Nuts, Bolts	Inspect and Tighten	x			
Controls	Inspect	x			
Air Filter	Clean	x			
	Replace		x		
Sawdust Guard	Clean	x			
Chain	Inspect and Sharpen	x			
Chain Break	Clean and Inspect	x			
Bar	Clean and Turn	x			
Shock Mounts	Inspect	x			
	Replace*				x
Sprocket	Inspect	x			
	Replace				x
Fuel Filter	Clean		x		
Oil Screen	Clean		x		
Muffler	Clean				x
Spark Arrestor Screen	Clean	x			
Spark Plug	Clean and Adjust		x		
	Replace				x
Cylinder Fins	Clean			x	
Starter Rope	Inspect		x		
	Replace				x
Carburetor	Clean*			x	
Fuel Tank	Clean			x	
Breaker Points	Clean and Adjust			x	
Lamination Gap	Clean and Adjust*			x	
Exhaust Ports	Clean			x	
Fuel, Oil and Pressure Hoses	Check*	x			x
Carburetor Diaphragm	Replace Once A Year*				
Crankshaft Seals	Replace Once A Year*				

*Recommended for maintenance by an authorized service dealer.

INCH/MILLIMETER CONVERSIONS

INCHES TO MILLIMETERS
Multiply inches by 25.4

MILLIMETERS TO INCHES
Multiply millimeters by 0.03937

INCHES	MILLIMETERS	INCHES	MILLIMETERS	MILLIMETERS	INCHES
.001	.025	17/32	13.4938	.001	.00004
.01	.254	35/64	13.8906	.01	.00039
1/64	.3969	9/16	14.2875	.02	.00079
.02	.508	37/64	14.6844	.03	.00118
.03	.762	19/32	15.0812	.04	.00157
1/32	.7938	.6	15.24	.05	.00196
.04	1.016	39/64	15.4781	.06	.00236
3/64	1.191	5/8	15.875	.07	.00276
.05	1.27	41/64	16.2719	.08	.00315
.06	1.524	21/32	16.6688	.09	.00354
1/16	1.5875	43/64	17.0656	.1	.00394
.07	1.778	11/16	17.4625	.2	.00787
5/64	1.9844	.7	17.78	.3	.01181
.08	2.032	45/64	17.8594	.4	.01575
.09	2.286	23/32	18.2562	.5	.01969
3/32	2.3812	47/64	18.6531	.6	.02362
.1	2.54	3/4	19.050	.7	.02756
7/64	2.7781	49/64	19.4469	.8	.0315
1/8	3.175	25/32	19.8438	.9	.03543
9/64	3.5719	51/64	20.2406	1.0	.03937
5/32	3.9688	.8	20.32	2.0	.07874
11/64	4.3656	13/16	20.6375	3.0	.11811
3/16	4.7625	53/64	21.0344	4.0	.15748
.2	5.08	27/32	21.4312	5.0	.19685
13/64	5.1594	55/64	21.8281	6.0	.23622
7/32	5.5562	7/8	22.225	7.0	.27559
15/64	5.9531	57/64	22.6219	8.0	.31496
1/4	6.35	.9	22.86	9.0	.35433
17/64	6.7469	29/32	23.0188	1 CM	.3937
9/32	7.1438	59/64	23.4156	2 CM	.7874
19/64	7.5406	15/16	23.8125	3 CM	1.1811
.3	7.62	61/64	24.2094	4 CM	1.5748
5/16	7.9375	31/32	24.6062	5 CM	1.9685
21/64	8.3344	63/64	25.0031	6 CM	2.3622
11/32	8.7312	1.0	25.4	7 CM	2.7559
23/64	9.1281	2.0	50.8	8 CM	3.1496
3/8	9.525	3.0	76.2	9 CM	3.5433
25/64	9.9219	4.0	101.6	1 DM	3.937
.4	10.16	5.0	127.0	2 DM	7.874
13/32	10.3188	6.0	152.4	3 DM	11.811
27/64	10.7156	7.0	177.8	4 DM	1 Ft., 3.748
7/16	11.1125	8.0	203.2		
29/64	11.5094	9.0	228.6		
15/32	11.9062	10.0	254.0		
31/64	12.3031	11.0	279.4		
1/2	12.7	1 Ft.	304.8		
33/64	13.0969				

ABBREVIATIONS
MM-Millimeter(1/1000)
CM-Centimeter(1/100)
DM-Decimeter(1/10)

Index